THE BIRTH OF LANGUAGE
The Case History of a Non-verbal Child

THE BIRTH OF LANGUAGE

The Case History of a Non-verbal Child

By

SHULAMITH KASTEIN

Director, Speech and Hearing Clinic
Columbia Presbyterian Medical Center
Lecturer in Otolaryngology
College of Physicians and Surgeons
Columbia University
New York, New York

and

BARBARA TRACE

With a Foreword by

SIDNEY CARTER, M.D.

Professor of Neurology
College of Physicians and Surgeons
Columbia University
New York, New York

CHARLES C THOMAS • PUBLISHER
Springfield • Illinois • U.S.A.

Published and Distributed Throughout the World by
CHARLES C THOMAS • PUBLISHER
BANNERSTONE HOUSE
301-327 East Lawrence Avenue, Springfield, Illinois, U.S.A.
NATCHEZ PLANTATION HOUSE
735 North Atlantic Boulevard, Fort Lauderdale, Florida, U.S.A.

With THOMAS BOOKS careful attention is given to all details of manufacturing and design. It is the Publisher's desire to present books that are satisfactory as to their physical qualities and artistic possibilities and appropriate for their particular use. THOMAS BOOKS will be true to those laws of quality that assure a good name and good will.

Printed in the United States of America
RV-10

FOREWORD

Delay in the development of language is often a significant and frequently an ominous sign of nervous system impairment. It can be a reflection of diffuse neurological involvement or be the result of a relatively circumscribed one. The presence of a serious speech problem in early childhood implies future social and psychological difficulties. Many school children with reading problems and many with behavior disorders have a history of delayed or impaired speech. It is a frequent early indication of mental retardation but can be associated with normal and sometimes, superior intellect.

In this book, Shulamith Kastein and Barbara Trace have detailed the case history of a non-verbal child from birth to the age of eleven years. Joan was born prematurely in the sixth month of her mother's pregnancy and weighed two pounds and three ounces at birth. She failed to develop language, had perceptual difficulties and exhibited behavior disorder. Early recognition of her basic problem and hours of daily work over many years helped overcome her disabilities. She was fortunate in having normal intellect, an understanding family, and the dedicated interest of two unusual women.

Mrs. Kastein, the Speech Pathologist at the Columbia Presbyterian Medical Center in New York, is a professional with vast experience in the area of language disorders. Mrs. Trace, the mother of the involved child and a woman with courage, faith and persistence, is an amateur in this field. These two ladies joined forces in producing a readable and informative book. The meaning of language and methods of identifying the cause of its deficiency are discussed. The techniques used in rehabilitation are given in great detail.

Joan had a very severe language defect. Youngsters with some variation of her difficulties are seen frequently in pediatric practice and attend many of our schools. This book makes for a better understanding of such children.

SIDNEY CARTER, M.D.

New York, New York

v

ACKNOWLEDGMENTS

GRATITUDE IS EXPRESSED to the many people who had contact with Joan, especially:

The late Edmund P. Fowler, Jr., M.D., Otologist, for his interest, his unfailing support and contributions to the study of children with communication disorders.

Donald R. Hirsch, M.D., Pediatrician, for his astute observation and inestimable advice.

Zelda S. Klapper, Ph.D., Psychologist, without whose guidance and professional acumen the case of Joan would be incomplete.

Sylvia Morgan, M.A., Pediatric Audiologist, for her skill in audiological management.

John S. Wortley, Ed.D., Speech Pathologist, for his contribution to Joan's progress and his splendid spirit of cooperation.

Profound indebtedness is expressed to Edith Bloch, MSW, Doris T. Leberfeld, Ed.D., and John D. Rainer, M.D., for their critical reading of the manuscript and their invaluable comments and editorial suggestions.

Thanks are due to Payne Thomas for his encouragement and assistance.

S.K.
B.T.

CONTENTS

PART III

THE BIRTH OF LANGUAGE

The Case History of a Non-verbal Child

PART ONE

INTRODUCTION AND PROLOGUE
Shulamith Kastein

INTRODUCTION

W E D O N O T U S U A L L Y speak of the birth of language. Language develops almost imperceptively, without conscious awareness or effort on the part of the child or his environment. It is only when language fails to develop that we realize what a complex process it is and what intricate patterns of integration within the nervous system have to be established to allow verbal communication to emerge. The child so affected may then show not only impairment in language and speech but impairment in other aspects of his development. Joan was such a child and her story is the story of the labor of love, courage and persistence on the part of an unusual mother and child, that eventually brought forth speech.

The mother, at the beginning of this story, had asked the question so often heard in doctors' offices and speech clinics, "Why does my child not speak? What can I do to help?" She asked until an answer was found. This mother, who accepted the answer (the diagnosis), and who considered every suggestion, every hint that assisted her in helping her child, became herself a competent therapist, without detracting from her role as a mother.

When at last the goal was reached and speech was born as a result of devotion and hard work, I suggested that she write her story, which is *The Story of Joan.*

I hoped she might share some of her experiences and observations with other parents of similarly impaired children and with professional workers whose responsibility they are. I did not know at that time how keen an observer and how splendid a recorder Mrs. Trace would be.

The Story of Joan, as written by her mother, is a unique document since it describes the difficulties, the problems and behavior characteristics of a child with language and behavior disorders. It provides all the details the professional observer, in the limited time spent with a patient, can only deduce and supports those of us who have known many of these children with proof that our assumptions were valid.

5

Joan's story also points out the need for early diagnosis of the child with communication disorders and early therapeutic management as well as parent counselling.

The Story of Joan should be of interest to members of many professional disciplines such as the pediatrician, the pediatric neurologist, the pediatric psychiatrist, the otologist, psychologist, speech pathologist and audiologist, as well as to social workers, teachers in special education, and so forth, and to parents of children with communication disorders.

Although there are many children with similar impairments, it must be stressed at the start that not every child responds in the same way Joan did. Nor can or should every mother of such a child be expected to take upon herself the task, or indeed should she be expected to be equipped to carry out such a program. However, *The Story of Joan* furnishes proof that it can be done, and how, in this case, it was achieved.

"My child does not talk. Why? What can I do to help my child?" This question, asked by anguished mothers, reflects their concern about the child's failure to develop speech which they intuitively feel to be the most important acquisition and the indispensible sign of normalcy. It is true that many children have a late start in speech development and require no special attention, but the mother frequently knows when her child is in serious trouble. Unfortunately, her urgency is often met with professional indifference and she is advised to relax and stop worrying. She is often told that the three-year old is too young to be diagnosed and "to come back in a year." If the child's behavior is obviously abnormal, she might be advised to seek psychiatric treatment for herself, often without further investigation of the child. In some of these cases the question to be raised is not "What has the mother done to the child?" but "What does an impaired child do to the mother and to the mother-child relationship?"

All too often, lack of speech development, failure of the child to understand spoken language—especially when combined with abnormal behavior manifestations—deserves and requires thorough study of the child and prompt decision on the therapeutic management. If this is not done, further interference with the child's development may not be averted. A therapeutic program is essential or the child may not be able to cope with the demands of an environment that does not know his basic problem, or ignores it. He then may become too frustrated to function even within his potential abilities or too impaired to benefit from school experience. If neglected, the child may become the non-reader, the non-speller who soon may be the non-performer or the delinquent child. Such a child may be further traumatized by his failure to communicate, by the reaction of his environment to his failure, and soon may be inextricably caught in the net of internal and external emotional conflicts.

Similarly, the development of the language impaired child who cannot understand spoken language, even when endowed with normal intelligence, may soon become retarded because he lacks the means of acquiring information about the world around him and the tools to develop his intellect.

The language impaired, disorganized child who does not look at the mother's face, who cannot interpret gestures or pantomine, or comprehend spoken words, misses the expression and often the intonational accents of the mother's love. He fails to receive information; explanations and warnings do not reach him. As a result, he may fail to establish contact with his environment and his personality development may be distorted. Fears and terror no one can relieve may drive the child into panic.

The non-verbal child who *understands* but cannot *use* speech has no means of verbally expressing his fears and anxieties, his feelings and thoughts. He may have to resort to deviant behavior as the only means available to him to relieve frustration and assert himself. If he has no speech he lacks the ability to verbally control himself and he may become more disinhibited and more difficult to manage.

In either case, language impairment may interfere with the child's ability to understand his environment and to develop a sense of self.

The entire organism is involved in verbal communication. The nervous system, endocrine functions, muscle tone, the intellect, environmental factors, emotion, personality traits, and so on, all are reflected in the manner in which we express ourselves. Indeed, they determine whether or not we can or wish to communicate, the words we choose, the sentences we form and the voice we use.

The very attempt to study these separate components, to define and to name them, detracts from what we are studying. We can only hope to approach our goal if we keep this fact in mind as a constant frame of reference. After having traced the parts we must put them together and use them in the light of the unique human being we are trying to understand.

The differential diagnostic language evaluation of the child with developmental disorders requires the study of all aspects of development, as well as the manner in which the growing organism tries to cope with his impairment and what compensatory mechanisms he uses.

It is not surprising that young children with language disorders often are considered difficult to evaluate. Partially responsible for this difficulty is the fact that there are both qualitative and quantitative factors involved which must be the concern of the examiner. A bias in one or the other direction results in confusion. Anyone who is in a clinical setting or in a position to receive medical and paramedical reports on children with communication disorders must be impressed by this confusion. The burden of this dilemma, of course, is placed squarely upon the parent and the child who does not receive help at the time when it is most needed and when it might be most beneficial.

The speech pathologist has a unique function to fulfill in the differential diagnosis and management of the language, behavior and learning impaired child. The development of language may be both the contributory as well as the determining factor of the degree of normalcy which the child will attain. Early detection of disturbances in the language areas, therefore, is of the utmost diagnostic, prognostic and habilitative importance since they often are the first, and frequently the only indication of central nervous system deficit in the young child.

Why then the difficulty?

One of the pitfalls seems to be the erroneous equation of the pre-verbal with the non-verbal state. The child who fails to develop communication by the time he is two and a half or three years old has done so because something went wrong in the pre-verbal stage; because he was prevented from listening, looking, feeling—from becoming aware of his environment and of himself and failed to absorb the language to which he was exposed. His inability to respond to the environment, to listen and learn to understand spoken language and to realize that there is verbal communication, prevented him from entering or completing the pre-verbal state. Statements such as "He is too young" or

"Come back in a year" or "He will grow out of it," or else a referral of the mother to a psychiatrist, points to these basic misconceptions in various disciplines, medical as well as para-medical.

Another factor is the difficulty in reconciling the medical pathology and the clinical functional aspects of the condition. In the case of a child this is complicated further by the limited number of opportunities for microscopic study.

With regard to language functions, therefore, too much of what has been observed in adult language disorders (aphasia) has been taken as a frame of reference and applied without check or modification to the child, disregarding the devastating consequences of language disorders for the integrity of the development of personality, thinking processes and intelligence of the child.

In order to evaluate a child with communication disorders a thorough knowledge of early childhood development and familiarity with the range of developmental variations, temperaments, emotional adjustments or maladjustments of the "normal" verbal child are essential. A thorough knowledge of the characteristics and range of variations, typical of specific pathology, such as the deaf or the blind, the intellectually subnormal, the specifically brain damaged, the mentally ill, and so on, is necessary in order to recognize those symptoms in a child, which may reflect one or the other pathology.

In children such as Joan, the diagnosis of language disorder centers around the function and integration of the central nervous system as far as this can be done clinically. Each link of the interdependent progressive chain of events that leads to the acquisition of verbal language must be tested in order to detect those links which have failed to develop or those which are weak.

The exploration of the peripheral sense organs—hearing, sight and touch—is the starting point and is followed by the investigation of the child's ability to listen, look and feel, that is to attend to auditory, visual and kinesthetic stimuli—the prerequisite of sense perception. These in turn lead to the next link, concept formation. That is the ability of the young child to integrate what he hears, sees and feels into the concept of the object so perceived. This prelinguistic development helps the child to reach the next major developmental step, symbol behavior, namely the comprehension and use of pantomine, words and pictures, the symbolic representation of sensory experience. Memory, recall of sequences and patterns play a role in this development which is subserved by the auditory, visual and kinesthetic feedback loops. The integrity of this monitoring system determines the speed and accuracy with which language develops and progresses. A break or weakness in these links may seriously interfere with normal language and speech development. Joan had suffered impairment in all these functions.

In order to make optimum use of his sensory motor functions, the child must have at least a certain amount of intelligence. If his intellect is limited, his language and speech development will develop within this limitation. The language impairment, on the other hand, may further depress his intellectual functions if undetected and untreated. This possibility is foremost in the minds of parents of children with communication disorders and constitutes a serious threat to their future development.

Since language development is a function of communication, the child must be sufficiently well adjusted emotionally to want to communicate and must live in a psychological climate conducive to communication. The behavior observed in a child during evaluation, therefore, may suggest adverse environmental influences, neurotic trends in the child, emotional disturbance reactive to his handicap, organic behavior symptoms or psychopathology.

The questions to be answered are whether the language impairment or the personality disorder are primary, or whether they present two aspects of the same pathology, as in the case of Joan. This decision should rest with the findings and confirmations of all professional members of the team whose responsibility the language impaired child becomes.

To gain further information and to complete the picture of the total developmental levels attained by the child, psychomotor functions, that is body concept, spatial orientation, figure ground discrimination and visuo-motor functions must be explored. These are the areas which appear to be most sensitive to disturbances of the central nervous system and resultant language disorders, and thus a source of indispensable diagnostic information. It was these areas which were found to be impaired in Joan.

The exploration of the muscles of articulation, speech production (articulation of speech sounds) and voice may add further valuable findings. In the older child, reading, writing and arithmetic, sentence structure and grammar, as well as the ability to use abstract concepts have to be investigated.

The pre-natal, natal and post-natal history, the history of motor and social development as well as group experience, furnish the additional pieces which when put together will yield the final differential diagnostic profile.

Who are the children with these profiles? They fall into two major groups: those with positive histories, in whom neurological impairment or mental illness can be demonstrated, and those whose clinical history and findings are negative.

The first group comprises many survivors of premature birth; rubella or other infectious diseases during pregnancy; blood incompatibilities; it also includes children with inborn errors of metabolism; cerebral palsies; convulsive disorders; brain diseases; injuries to the brain; mental retardation, emotional illness and other pathologies, which also produce language disorders.

The second group consists of children in whom a substratum of non-demonstrable central nervous system deficit is subsumed, and whose only symptoms are language, speech and voice impairments, deviant behavior and learning disabilities.

PROLOGUE

JOAN IS A SURVIVOR of premature birth. Her first weeks of life were complicated by retrolental fibroplasia from which she recovered. The recovery marked the start of her excellent physical development which gave her parents every reason to expect no further complications. Their hopes for a normally developing child were soon shaken by the deviant behavior of their daughter, their third child, which was so different from that of her two brothers.

Joan did not respond to her parents or brothers. She failed to develop speech and defied attempts at communication or control.

Joan's history is interesting because so many of her behavior characteristics are typical of symptoms found in children with central nervous system deficit and language disorders. Her difficulties in her development show the devastating influence of central nervous system disorganization on the total development of personality, behavior and learning in a child.

I met Joan when she was four years and four months old. At that time she had had the benefit of six months of language therapy at a speech center.

Joan, when I first saw her, was a little girl who appeared very immature and overdependent on her mother from whom she could not be separated. She was grinding her teeth, was anxious, tense and negativistic. Although she was very withdrawn, some contact could be established and responses could be elicited.

Joan's comprehension of spoken language was extremely limited. She seemed sensitive to sound and would hold her ears when street noises reached her. While she could understand a few single words, she was unable to understand the same words when put into simple sentences. She was not able to answer any questions. She had conspicuous difficulty with abstract word forms such as "where, how, why, over, on top, under" and so on. Joan was unable to interpret pantomine and did not attempt to lip read, nor indeed could she be made to look at the speaker's face. There was echolalia and

12

perseveration—she repeated what was said without understanding or would continue giving the same response regardless of relevance. Although she could recognize some pictures, her difficulty in visual perception was obvious. As is often seen in children with language disorders, Joan could articulate those words which she had learned to understand, while words that were unfamiliar to her were produced with considerable articulatory deficiencies. Her sense of rhythm was exceedingly poor and she was unable to imitate the simplest pattern. She could not use toy objects in imaginative play.

Although she could use her hands well in handling objects, the pencil was held with poor coordination and with a mild tremor of the hand. Her attempt at copying a circle and a cross resulted in very poor execution. Her drawing of a person showed primitive and impaired body concept. Poor body concept was further demonstrated by her difficulty in identifying parts of her own body and a peculiar vagueness in her body movements and orientation in space.

Joan's language diagnostic profile indicated a child with severe receptive language disorder* as the major impairment and concomitant disorder in visual perception, body concept, visuo-motor functions, as well as poor coordination. The emotional immaturity, withdrawal tendencies and shallow affect were considered another aspect of the central nervous system syndrome. The uneven development and the depression of intellectual functions at that time were thought to be due to the language disorder and general disorganization since the child demonstrated good thinking and associative ability in some non-verbal areas. Peripheral hearing was considered grossly adequate.

The nature of Joan's disorder in communication made global planning of therapeutic management imperative.

Psychological testing of the child was postponed at that time since it was felt that the psychological test would not gauge the child's actual potential because of the interference of her poorly integrated central nervous system and the language and behavior disorder.

Therapy is the extension of the diagnostic profile and the attempt at restoring the missing links or strengthening the weak links

---

*This and similar conditions are often referred to as: Auditory agnosia, central auditory imperception, receptive aphasia or dysacusis—all terms to indicate that the impairment is not in the *peripheral* organ of hearing, rather that it is a *central* auditory dysfunction.

in the developmental chain, by training in the functions the child cannot develop unaided. The study of each child, therefore, determines the approach, the method and the material to be used as well as the psychological climate in which therapy is to be carried out.

Therapy in children must involve the parents. In order to help the child, the parents have to know what is wrong with the child and have to be helped to understand the symptoms as well as the behavior of the child in order to deal with it effectively and, indeed, to tolerate it.

It is well to remember in parent counselling that parents, as a result of their own experience, conditioning and preconceived ideas, have prejudices with regard to diagnostic categories. While one mother may express her fear of deafness and will readily accept any other diagnosis, another mother may admit that she could not tolerate the thought of having a retarded child, or a disturbed child, as the case may be, but would be reconciled with another pathology. These parents have to be helped to understand this and to be guided into accepting their children's condition.

Another aspect is the inability of parents to "hear" what has been told them. They may quite truthfully state that "Nobody ever told me what was wrong with my child." No matter how often they may have been told, they were not psychologically ready to accept the information and therefore actually did not hear it. This, too, has to be dealt with, preferably by talking with each parent and also with both parents together so that the stronger partner may help the weaker one to accept and understand the problem.

If the parent, especially the mother, is competent she should be part of the team concerned with the habilitation of the child. Only when therapeutic management can be extended into the home and become part of the daily routine will it be most effective. However, the precarious balance between a child's need for dependence, the necessity for reducing this need as the child gains a sense of self and increasing ability to function, has to be continuously re-established. If this is not done, a mother who must function for her impaired child may herself become dependent on the child's need for her. If she is not carefully guided and made aware of the boundaries between her own involvement and the child's changing needs, mother and child may become locked in an ever tighter bond of interdependence.

The mother who can actively contribute to her child's habilitation, may gain greater insight into the specific disabilities as well as understanding of her child's potential. In the case of Joan, this has been beautifully demonstrated.

The therapeutic management of Joan had to be all-inclusive. It ranged from the introduction of educational toys and activities geared at strengthening muscle coordination, to sense and perceptual training, daily living activities as well as communication. The mother was specifically advised how to encourage greater independence in the child and enhance emotional growth. Language therapy continued at the speech center and included training of body concept, visuo-motor functions, auditory memory and rhythm. Reduction of perseverative tendencies and echolalia was another aspect of the program.

Nursery school attendance was strongly recommended. It was hoped that this experience would enhance emotional and social growth and complement the sensory motor and language training.

During the seven years following this first visit, Joan and her parents were seen at intervals of several months with occasional telephone conferences between visits.

Looking at Joan's records, two recurrent themes stand out: emotional immaturity and difficulty in comprehension and retention of spoken and written language. Difficulty in dealing with abstract concepts has been a diminishing but constant problem. In addition, impaired body concept and visuo-motor dysfunctions played a significant role. The development in these areas is reflected in Joan's drawings (see appendix), the records of the Goodenough Drawing of a Man Test and the Bender Gestalt Test. These tests were administered regularly but were judged only qualitatively, not quantitatively.

At each return visit, Joan was given a complete language and speech evaluation. The links which had still been found weak or missing at preceding visits were retested and an assessment was made of the gains in response to the special training she received and in relation to her chronological growth.

No one test, indeed not any number of tests adequately serve the task of testing a child like Joan. In addition to formal tests, each area of dysfunction, each clue must be followed and probed and related to the child's total behavior. Often the means of achieving this must be invented on the spur of a fleeting moment; the moment which might reveal a most significant clue.

At first, Joan needed help in becoming aware of herself before she could relate to and eventually communicate with those around her. She had to learn to feel, look and listen. She had to be taught the meaning of each word. Everything had to be reduced to its simplest and most concrete denominator before she could comprehend it. Language had to be fed slowly and built step by step and slowly, over the years, the chain of development, broken in so many places at first, was restored.

Although Joan had always demonstrated that she could hear, an attempt at testing her hearing had been made when she was three years and ten months old. While she did not respond to standard testing procedures, her reactions indicated "grossly adequate hearing, sufficient for the development of speech."

Since children with receptive language disorders, that is *central* auditory dysfunctions, may also have a hearing loss or acquire it, Joan's hearing remained suspect and under surveillance. It was not until she was seven and a half years old, however, when her reactions to environmental sounds and some of her speech patterns indicated some hearing problem in addition to her difficulty in comprehension of speech. She was referred to an otologist for an examination of her ears and to a pediatric audiologist for a complete hearing evaluation. The physical findings were negative, the diagnosis was dysacusis and hypoacusis (central and peripheral auditory impairment). The pure tone hearing tests, which now could be administered in standard fashion, showed a mild loss in the low frequencies and an abrupt drop in the high frequencies. Amplification was tried but Joan could not tolerate it and the recommendation for a hearing aid was postponed. Two years later Joan had gained enough emotional stability and control to adjust to the wearing of a hearing aid. The aid, in addition to amplifying especially the high frequency tones the child could not hear well, served to help her focus on speech. A small hearing tube used in her training program had served this function until this time. Alerting her to sound and the resulting attention to spoken language proved to be the greatest benefit she has derived from the hearing aid since.

Joan's speech, a source of concern to her parents at times, reflected her difficulty with auditory patterns, sound sequences and her poor auditory memory. As Joan acquired more language, her emotional problems were reflected in her speech by whining, monotony and mumbling. Later, her difficulty with high frequency sounds reflected a hearing loss in this frequency range. At one time, an orthodontic problem contributed to additional slight distortions in her speech. She has since received orthodontic treatment. The small hearing tube had previously also been used to correct articulatory deficiencies.

Joan's intellectual ability was evaluated in school during her kindergarten year in order to determine whether she was intellectually capable of coping with the academic program of the first grade. Her records and class observations resulted in the promotion into first grade.

When Joan was nine years and five months old, she had progressed sufficiently to warrant a complete psychological evaluation by standardized tests to determine her relative intellectual standing in relation to children her own age.

A test battery was administered by a psychologist. Following are excerpts from her report:

> Normal intellectual function was evident in the test score as well as in the quality of Joan's responses.
>
> Reasoning ability is evident in the instances in which the child was required to select relevant items from her recollection of her own experience and apply these memory items to a new situation. She showed an eager organized attitude toward such problems, and a range of success directly related to the extent to which language was involved. In items in which an abstract grasp of language was involved—either in the understanding of the situation or in the formation of the response—there was less success than in situations which either did not depend on language, or used language in a direct and personally meaningful way. She compared favorably with her age group with respect to the latter type of item; she does not compare favorably with her peers when confronted with situations involving social comprehension in an impersonal context, or abstract problems presented in a verbal setting.
>
> The areas in which Joan excelled are not the ones generally tapped by standardized intelligence tests: Memory is excellent. Her work habits and her approach to test situations are marvelous; she is well motivated and eager to succeed and has good learning potential. Adhering to the test material itself, it is unlikely that her over-all scores will improve considerably in the succeeding years unless there is a marked development in the area of abstract language functioning.

This report supports an observation often made in clinical experience. Some children with impairment in language, perceptional functions and learning, when given special training in the impaired areas, do better than their non-impaired contemporaries.

At each visit, an interval history was taken and the parents' impression of Joan's response to the home training program, behavior achievement in school and daily living experience was discussed. The parents' rating of her progress and their concern about the future of the child were the basis for the measure of support and reassurance they were given. Occasionally, a warning had to be sounded to reduce the pressure and allow the child more freedom.

In planning the therapeutic program for a child, the mother's personality and emotional needs must be taken into consideration. In the case of Joan, the mother's strength and ability to invest so much of herself in the child's training without detriment to herself was used. It served both mother and child well.

PART TWO

THE STORY OF JOAN
Barbara Trace

Chapter 1

A BABY IS BORN

Our baby was born on October twenty-third, nineteen hundred and fifty-three, three months and one week before she was due to arrive. At birth she weighed two pounds and three ounces (nine hundred and eighty-five grams) and measured fourteen inches (thirty-five centimeters) in length. There was no indication during my brief, uneventful pregnancy that it would be prematurely terminated.

During the hours of mild labor that preceded the baby's arrival, I feared that this pregnancy might result in a miscarriage. I had, thus far, been successful in bringing only two of five pregnancies to full term. I was not given any anesthesia during the delivery. All precautions were taken to safeguard the baby. The birth process was rapid and normal. When it was over, I saw a curled up, red faced, infinitesimally tiny girl sitting in the palm of the obstetrician's hand. To my great surprise, she was very much alive. The staff pediatrician put her into an incubator at once.

Within a short time, I was returned to my room. My obstetrician came to see me, and told me that my baby was apparently normal and healthy. He discussed the critical nature of the first twenty-four hours in the baby's life, and prognosticated that it would be weeks before she would be out of danger. Before leaving, he added an ominous post-script. He said that if our little girl lived, she had a good chance of developing a condition that could cause her to be blind.

Even before he spoke to me of this, I had recalled poignant stories about the unusually high incidence, in premature infants, of an eye condition that sometimes caused severe impairment of their vision. I had read that there was no cure for it, and that its causes were not known to the medical profession. As my obstetrician spoke, my heretofore vague fears crystallized. His words were, for me, tantamount to pronouncing a sentence of blindness on our little girl. I became so extremely upset that I required sedation for the three days I remained in the hospital.

At frequent intervals during the day, I received bulletins about the baby's general condition. She survived the first twenty-four hours, and thereafter held her own in her battle for life. I was in great conflict about these reports. One thought seemed to dominate all others. Even though I had looked forward very much to having this baby, I only wanted her to survive if she could be healthy and normal in every respect. Blindness seemed to me to be the greatest affliction that could befall her. I could not achieve any perspective about this. The anxiety and feelings of guilt I had about bringing her prematurely into the world had seriously disturbed my normal sense of values.

I shared my thoughts fully with my husband. He too was sad and deeply concerned about the baby, but he tried to reassure me. I remained inconsolable.

On the third miserable day after my baby's birth, when I was scheduled to go home, I finally summoned up enough courage to consider going to the nursery to visit my little girl. This was something I had been avoiding until now because the prospect of seeing her frightened me. I had had a brief glimpse of her at birth, but had not seen her long enough to know what she really looked like. Many questions plagued me. How far had her development proceeded? Would she be completely formed? Would I see a real baby?

Combined with this anxiety was the ever growing conflict within me as to whether I wanted her or not. The choice, of course, was clearly not mine since she was here, but, nonetheless, I continued to struggle with this powerful emotion.

Finally, I decided that I had dallied long enough. Distraught as I was, I began to feel very ashamed of my cowardice, and I went to her.

In the nursery, I could scarcely control myself as I gazed at this tiny, helpless human being whose head was no larger than the size of an orange. I stared in disbelief at her perfectly formed body, and watched her move actively about in her carefully regulated Isolette protected from possible capricious changes in temperature and humidity. I stayed only a very short time because I was so upset. As I was leaving, a kind nurse tried to reassure me, but I scarcely reacted. She showed me photographs of grown up "preemies." However, I was too submerged in self pity, anxiety, and pessimism to derive much comfort from them.

I was discharged promptly after the visit. It was so good to get away from all the happy, excited mothers and beautiful full term babies I saw all about me in the hospital. How I envied them.

Chapter 2

I RETURN HOME ALONE

I HAD MISSED MY HUSBAND and sons very much, and I was very glad to be back home with them. Our boys were only two and one-half and five years old, respectively, and still needed much care. I had always enjoyed being with them because they were delightfully healthy and bright. My husband and I decided not to tell them about their new sister until we had some assurance that she would live. I went about my duties mechanically, trying to renew my interest in my family and home. I continued to be terribly despondent, but I somehow managed to hide my feelings from the boys. To the best of my knowledge, they were not conscious of a crisis in our family.

In the evenings, when my husband returned from work, I released the emotions I had held carefully in check all day. Although my husband tried to help me regain some balance and objectivity, I think I was more successful in depressing him. No one could really help me at this time because I was looking for positive assurance that our little girl would not be a victim of retrolental fibroplasia,* the eye condition we feared so much. We tried to find out all we could about this dreadful condition in the vain hope that we would find evidence that would exclude her from the group that acquired it. We read everything on the subject we could find. With horror, we found confirmation of our most dreaded fears. The literature was full of statistics about the high incidence of retrolental fibroplasia in premature infants of our baby's birth weight. We learned too, that if it ran its full course, and blindness or near blindness resulted, normal vision could not be restored. We found out that in some cases the condition reversed itself before permanent damage set in. In these situations, normal or near normal eye development continued. However, we could not believe that our baby would be one of the fortunate ones.

---

*We learned that retrolental fibroplasia was a disease of the eye first described in 1942, affecting premature infants and often resulting in blindness. Its pathology consisted of proliferation of blood vessels and fibrous tissue between the lens and the retina.

We were convinced that she, a qualified statistical candidate for this condition, would acquire it, and that it would run its full destructive course.

Each day, at a prearranged time, I called the hospital for a brief medical report about our baby. I waited numbly to hear the results of any eye examinations she might have had, what her latest weight was, and a brief description of her general appearance.

During the first ten days, our baby's weight gradually went down to one pound and nine ounces (seven hundred and twenty grams). She had no difficulty breathing, and needed a mixture of oxygen and air only intermittently for the first ten days. After that, the oxygen was permanently removed. Thereafter, for her stay of a total of twelve weeks, she maintained a steady daily gain of approximately ten to fifteen grams. Her color was good, and she never experienced any crisis that threatened her life. The doctors reported that all aspects of her development were proceeding normally, and as the days passed, we had every expectation that she would continue to thrive.

Feeding was done initially by tube, but she was given a bottle as soon as the nurses were able to remove her from the Isolette for brief periods without endangering her life.

Our baby remained in the Isolette for eight weeks, and was then transferred to a bassinet in the nursery for four more weeks. The eight weeks in the Isolette were emotionally barren and cold. Our little girl was deprived of the usual warm expressions of love a baby normally receives when she is fondled and held for feedings. I suspect that those weeks in isolation played some negative role in her subsequent development. However, the nurses had no choice, because excessive handling during those early weeks would have burned up too many of her calories, and she had none to spare.

She was very well cared for, and the nurses reported to me that she always took her feedings eagerly. From the very beginning, she seemed to manifest great strength of will. For example, she constantly maneuvered herself to a favored corner of the Isolette despite the nurses' efforts to keep her comfortable in the center. Also, when she was transferred out of the Isolette to the nursery, she rejected the care of a particular nurse whom she seemed to dislike. This was the only nurse out of a large staff from whom she refused to take feedings. Was this a forecast of the kind of personality we would have to deal with in the future?

During her three month stay in the hospital, we visited her from time to time. Despite my attempts to control my feelings, I loved her a little more each time I saw her. The condition of her eyes remained unknown, and I continued to be very perturbed about it. However, I must have been making some small progress in adjusting to the idea that her eyes might be severely damaged because I began to say to my friends, "If only she sees a little, how fortunate I will feel. I will love her and care for her with all my heart." Actually, I had not one shred of hope that her eyes would escape being seriously impaired.

A staff ophthalmologist examined our baby regularly, and gave us censored reports of his findings. It was not until we were almost ready to take her home, that we learned the facts. She had indeed developed retrolental fibroplasia when she was three weeks old, but it had started to regress almost immediately thereafter. I cannot describe our joy when we found out that the condition had come and gone, and that the prognosis for the future looked excellent. We were instantly restored to sanity and peace.

At no other time during this early period had we had any other concerns about our baby's development. From our conversations with doctors and from our reading and general knowledge, we had learned that if a premature baby is healthy and does not develop this eye condition, there should be no special problems connected with the infant's development. We knew of no other condition that could prevent her from progressing normally. Little did we suspect what the future held in store for us.

We began our happy preparations for our baby's homecoming. We told the boys about their new sister and talked of our "three" children for the first time. At this point we named our baby. We called her Joan. I do not really know why we had not named her until now, but I can conjecture. Perhaps, for us, the giving of a name would have denoted acceptance of her as a member of our family. There were subtle as well as overt reasons why we could not fully accept her. First, her hold on life initially was very tenuous, and we knew that she could slip away at any time. Then, I had never held her in my arms, and, therefore, she did not really seem to belong to me. Also, and most important of all, I was so frightened about the condition of her eyes that I unconsciously denied the reality that she was here and that she was mine. Happily, all this was now resolved.

On January sixteenth, nineteen hundred and fifty-four, when Joan was exactly twelve weeks old, she was discharged from the hospital. She weighed five pounds and four ounces (two thousand three hundred and eighty grams), and measured nineteen inches (forty six centimeters) in length. We needed to wait another brief period in order to find out whether there was any residual eye damage.

Six weeks later, the same ophthalmologist who had examined her in the hospital visited her. After a thorough eye examination, he told us that Joan's eyes were entirely normal. We had been granted a total reprieve.

Chapter 3

JOAN AT HOME

AT HOME, JOAN RESPONDED well to the physical care I was giving her. Her appetite and health were excellent. Because of her small body weight, she required frequent daytime and nighttime bottles. Joan had a feeding approximately every two hours. When she was about six or seven months old, she was big enough to take larger quantities of liquid and solid foods during the day and consequently did not need night bottles any longer. She then slept well throughout the night.

While her physical responses were excellent, her emotional ones were very unsettled. From the beginning, Joan exhibited extreme tension. She was anxious before and after feedings, woke up tense and disgruntled after a full night of sleep, mouthed toys and rattles frantically, and rejected all fondling. When she was six months old, she began to smile and respond to some stimuli such as people smiling at her, clucking at her, or playing with her. However, these moments of sunshine were brief and fleeting. For the most part, she cried and fussed, and seemed unable to derive any comfort from being held, caressed, or rocked. All attempts on our part to adjust her schedule, food intake, or care, in order to improve the situation, failed.

Although this was markedly different from my experience with our two sons, I was not concerned at first. I was essentially relaxed and confident because I felt that I was an experienced and competent mother. I attributed Joan's unusual behavior to the fact that she had had an extraordinary start in life. Furthermore, I understood the concept of individual difference and did not expect Joan to respond in just the same way her brothers had. I could only conclude that Joan had needs which I could not interpret as yet. I was hopeful that, if I worked hard enough at it, the whole picture would eventually become clearer to me. I intensified my efforts to understand her better. I devoted myself very diligently to her care.

Still, as the months passed, I found that I was making no headway. I became more perplexed and harassed, but I was still not

28

discouraged. It was obvious that Joan was not in contact with me or with her environment. I considered this to be a reflection of a slower maturing process, and expected her to calm down as soon as she could understand herself and her environment better. To this end, I provided her with a consistent routine, gentle loving care, a calm atmosphere, and abundant attention. I tried to define limits and administer necessary disciplines.

Joan was a restless, driven child involved largely in seemingly aimless, frustrating, destructive activity. She could not or would not accept limits. She did not respond to discipline. We could not determine whether this was due to lack of understanding or defiance. Since we could not reach her in a reasonable way, we protected her from situations that were potentially dangerous by physically removing her from them. She was very determined though, and usually tried to return to whatever had occupied her. Restraining her brought on massive tantrums. These scenes of rage occurred steadily through the day. Sometimes they were triggered by a specific situation, but more often, they were not based on anything discernible or comprehensible to us. Her crying dominated the scene during the first two years of her life, and we usually did not know what precipitated it or what stopped it. I began to be convinced that neither she nor I knew what she needed or wanted. Her expression of her needs baffled me completely, and as a result, my interpretation of her wants usually was incorrect.

While the emotional picture deteriorated, Joan's physical development continued to be satisfactory. Although it was a little slower than that of a full term baby, there was steady progress. She was always very active, but could not turn over until she was eight months old. When she was twelve months old, the pediatrician's report read as follows: "sits up well, bright, sees well, coordination good, excellent weight and growth progress." Joan's first tooth appeared when she was eleven months old, and at twelve months, she sat up well enough to eat in her baby chair. Between the ages of twelve and fifteen months, Joan stood up while supporting herself in her bed or in her play pen. At eighteen months, she was crawling actively, standing well without support, and climbing. It was, however, not until six months later, when Joan was twenty-four months old, that she could walk by herself. She was rather poorly coordinated at first, and fell quite often.

In contrast to Joan's poor control of her large muscles, her small muscles were developing well. Between the ages of one and two, her manipulative skill and competence increased rapidly and steadily. She could, at the age of two, feed herself competently, dress herself partially, and handle Holgate and Child Guidance toys such as blocks, cones, and trains skillfully. If she dismantled a toy, she could usually reassemble it with a dexterity which was beyond what one would expect to see in a child of this age. Observing her as she handled toys and household objects, we judged her performance to be superior. However, her span of attention was very brief, and she raced frantically from one activity to another.

Joan, at the age of two, was maturing well physically, but was not developing properly into a social being.

Chapter 4

A VERY DIFFICULT TIME

THE PERIOD THAT FOLLOWED, when Joan was between two and three and one-half years old, stands out in my mind as the most stormy and baffling that I have ever experienced. My constant expectation that she would grow more independent and begin to respond to controls was not fulfilled. She remained excessively egocentric.

Joan's behavior became more difficult. As she became stronger and more robust, she also became more active, frustrated, and dependent. Her movements were quicker, her temper remained violent, her capacity for destruction increased, and her crying scarcely ever ceased. Occasionally, she would smile brightly in response to some funny antics on our part, but her behavior was still largely unpredictable and hostile.

If I looked away from her during mealtime, she banged her head on the table until she had my attention again. She often turned her plate upside down on her head or on the floor, and blackmailed me into offering rewards such as a different play thing for each mouthful she took. Joan succeeded in manipulating me because I felt I had to get some food into her. Food acted as a sedative and gave us brief peaceful respites from her almost constant rage.

One of the essential qualities that seemed to be seriously lacking in Joan was the ability to anticipate anything in her environment. She could not recognize, recall, or understand its form and structure. She seemed to be whirling about in a vacuum. I look back now at this period and think about how frightened she must have been. She seemed to be a desolate human being.

To help establish direction and pattern, we scarcely varied Joan's routine from day to day. It was well ordered, with all activities such as meals, bath, snacks, outdoor play, naps, and bedtime scheduled. Yet, she looked upon each new day with bewilderment.

We avoided introducing any situation that might confuse or upset her. The boys were quiet youngsters and did not bother Joan. I was the only one who ever took care of her with the exception of my husband who substituted for me on Saturday afternoons when I went shopping. She responded with her father in the same way she did with me. Even though our home was always kept as free of noise and con-flict as possible, Joan continued to be in a nearly constant state of agitation and hyperactivity.

There was one dramatic exception. At night, exhausted and fortu-nately aware of the function of a bed, Joan fell asleep quickly and slept peacefully through the night.

It was an intensely stressful period, but it was not entirely with-out some small positives. Joan was a pretty child with blond curls, bright eyes, and a sturdy, well proportioned body. She laughed when her brothers clowned around, and it was then that we momentarily forgot her habitual disruptive behavior. Unfortunately though, her face usually clouded over again very soon, and the situation became in-tolerable once more.

I remember her naptime in particular detail. It was then that she ran through a maze that never varied from day to day. I lay her down in her crib, kissed her, and left the room. Before the door was closed, she scrambled up, and began rocking her crib to various parts of the room. Methodically, she pulled down all the toys stacked on her heavily laden toy shelves, and hurled them in all directions about the room. I could trace her progress as I listened to the noises which came through to the room below. She then navigated her crib to her next goal. Down came the tie backs on the curtains, and the lamp which was on top of her chest of drawers. Last of all, she pulled the nursery plaques off the wall, removed her sheet and pad from her bed, tossed them on the floor, and went to sleep for at least two hours.

Joan almost always woke up crying, and she looked pathetically confused when I scolded her about what she had done to her room. Although I expressed anger each time I saw this damage, she did not react in any way to my words or the emotion I exhibited. She did not seem to understand me. My scolding did not restrain her in any way from repeating her performance day after day.

I knew, of course, that I could strip Joan's room bare, and thus avoid the bedlam she created, but I was reluctant to do that. It would merely have served as an immediate solution to the problem, but would not have taught her what it was I expected of her in terms of acceptable behavior. Therefore, I restored her room each day to its original state, and continued to try to make contact with her.

On one particular occasion, Joan embarked on a rampage that surpassed all others. After unloading her toy shelves, she jockeyed up to the windows as usual. However, this time, she tore the curtains down and ripped them into shreds. When I went up to her room after naptime, she was surrounded by filmy bits of organdy. I was so furious at this wanton destruction that I spanked her very hard. She looked at me with an impassive expression on her face and did not even cry. Actually, the only time that Joan cried during a spanking was when it hurt her physically. This time, I apparently had not reached through her diaper clad bottom.

I was thoroughly miserable whenever I spanked her, and I did it infrequently. It actually accomplished nothing. After a while, it became abundantly clear that any form of discipline I administered, whether verbal or physical, was harsh and unjust. First of all, Joan seemed incapable of connecting cause and effect in this situation. Second, it seemed impossible to teach Joan because she was not in contact with me or anyone else in her environment long enough for that to be accomplished. To make matters even worse, Joan was not speaking at all as yet, and I could not determine whether or not she even understood my words.

My role, therefore, for the time being, was simply that of a caretaker. Although I was frequently hostile and angry at her, I tried to control myself as much as possible. I strove to deal rationally with this totally irrational human being. For the most part, I succeeded in remaining patient and calm. I loved Joan very much, and felt great responsibility for her.

When we resigned ourselves to the fact that we could not reach Joan yet through commonly accepted methods, we sought mechanical solutions to problems which we could not ignore. In the case of the naptime marathons, my husband found a way of anchoring the crib rigidly to the center of the room, and we installed guard rails to keep her in bed when she started climbing out of it. This really limited her activities. When I placed her in her crib, she watched me as I closed her door. Then she removed her sheet, tossed it on the floor, and immediately went to sleep. Thus, step-by-step, we handled whatever situations we could, and bided our time with those that could not be dealt with immediately. Dealing with Joan often taxed our ingenuity.

We sought and found the line of least resistance wherever and whenever possible.

I took Joan out in all kinds of weather when I realized that she loved being outdoors. Here, strangely enough, she could relax a little. She enjoyed the swings, the sandbox, and the slide, but she stayed with each activity for only a very brief period. Joan showed poor judgment generally about her own limitations and the limitations of the equipment she was using. I had to supervise her very carefully in order to avoid serious accidents.

Joan loved walking even more than playing in the playground. This was the only time in the day when her constant demands ceased. As we walked for miles along suburban roads, she would let me hold her hand, the only time I could do this for such a long period of time. In her other hand, she held a leaf or twig. She would stop now and then to exchange it for something else. I would talk to her and point to things, but she never responded in any way. I had no way of telling what this experience meant to her.

Although Joan was now three and one-half years old, she was still walking as an infant does, with her arms up and bent at the elbows to give her balance. She fell rather frequently, and cried bitterly even if the hurt was very minor. Here again, she showed her remoteness by not being able to understand my sympathy and concern.

It was impossible not to make comparisons between Joan's development and that of her brothers. Our sons had understood and accepted limits from the time they were very small children. They had always responded well to discipline. The normal self centeredness they had exhibited as infants had diminished as they began to understand the meaning of relationships. They were developing independence based on a strong sense of self, an awareness of their individuality, and a fast growing knowledge of right and wrong. Our sons were demonstrating an acceptance of their roles in relation to their total environment, and were establishing proper values.

Allowing for individual differences between our children, we strove to give Joan essentially the same kind of structure we were providing for her brothers. Our efforts thus far, had been seemingly ineffectual. Joan seemed to be involved solely in self gratification, and showed no signs of developing an integrated personality.

She did not, as yet, understand the most elementary meaning of relationship.

This serious lack was clearly demonstrated in her daily behavior with the members of her family. She did not seem to know who her father and I were. Certainly, we were important to her, but not as people. We were merely familiar structures like her bed or her play table that she clung to for her very existence. She expressed panic when either her father or I, depending upon who was caring for her at the time, disappeared even momentarily from her view. She showed no capacity for accepting or giving love. She never responded in any way to approval or disapproval. Joan seemed to be whirling about in space, without roots, and without contact. No noticeable lines of communication had been established.

Joan's behavior with her brothers and playmates had a somewhat different character. She was just as unrelated to them as to us, but she showed a good deal of aggression towards them. She liked having them physically near and smiled and laughed if they amused her. However, she often crept up behind them when they were occupied, and for no apparent reason, tried to hit them. I was, fortunately, usually able to thwart her because I watched her closely and anticipated her movements. In the playground, her companions quickly abandoned her because of the behavior she exhibited towards them, and she was left to play alone.

Joan tried to possess and then destroy her brothers' playthings. Restraining her brought forth tremendous temper tantrums. I was determined to guard the boys' rights, and this resulted in daily struggles with Joan. Her strength of purpose and her strength of body were herculean. I won merely because I was still bigger and stronger than she was.

I often worried about the boys' reactions to Joan. She, after all, dominated the family scene. I wondered how they could possibly accept this. However, they never expressed anything negative in their behavior or attitude towards her, even when she harassed them. They seemed ready to accept Joan as long as her hostility to them was controlled. Joan's abandoned flights through the house, her defiance of controls, her unpredictable temper outbursts, and mistreatment of property generally added up to a three ring circus. I rather think that the boys enjoyed some of the wild capers they witnessed. It is interesting that Joan tampered only with those things that seemed to have personal meaning for her like her toys, her brothers' toys, food, kitchen utensils, and the furnishings of her room. She showed no interest whatsoever in disturbing other parts of the home like ornaments, lamps, books, ashtrays, and so on.

During play, the boys treated Joan tenderly and lovingly. When she hit them, they merely walked away from her saying quietly, "She is only a baby and does not understand." Over and over again, my husband and I observed, that as long as our sons were assured of our loyalty and devotion to them, Joan could not threaten them.

Another deep concern that I had was whether I was expressing my love for the boys sufficiently, and giving them as much attention as they needed. Joan was so demanding of my time and energies that very little of me seemed left to give. Alert to the possibility that problems could develop, I observed them carefully. However, I found them to be loving, secure, and well adjusted. They expressed a great deal of affection for us, and continued to develop in a healthy way.

We sought constantly to reduce, wherever possible, the tension and friction between Joan and us. We could not, for example, continue to battle with her constantly about keeping away from her brothers' property. Therefore, we tried barring her physically from their rooms, and instructed them to guard their possessions carefully. This was, admittedly, an unhappy set of circumstances, but it accomplished its objective. It narrowed the battlefield and decreased the number of conflicts between Joan and the rest of us. We knew that we had to maintain these restrictions and many others until Joan learned to accept limits, and began to recognize and respect the rights of others.

Joan's contacts outside of the family were minimal, but those who knew her reacted positively to her. She had developed a good deal of charm. As time passed, her smiles came more readily in response to smiles from others, her postures became impish, and everyone found her physical attractiveness very appealing. Friends regarded any anti-social behavior they witnessed merely a reflection of poor home discipline. We knew this was not so. We plodded on with the ever growing conviction that something beyond our comprehension was amiss. We were gradually becoming aware of the fact that Joan was still, at approximately the age of three and one-half, very far from developing into a person. We were beginning to recognize that Joan was not going to change overnight from a disoriented human being into an integrated one. It was beginning to dawn upon us that any improvement in her behavior would depend upon the development of a faculty which was apparently absent.

Chapter 5

A DISCOVERY

THE REALIZATION OF WHAT was wrong came slowly, but at last, we acknowledged the fact that Joan had a calamitous deficiency. Until she was approximately three and one-half years old, she had practically no language comprehension. Not only was she not able to speak, but she appeared to be incapable of understanding concepts and words. She seemed unable to interpret gestures or to translate her own needs into gestures. Regardless of the method of communication, Joan was uncomprehending. Although this was a difficult quality to assess, my husband and I felt that this was unquestionably so.

If Joan was thirsty, hungry, tired, yearning to go outdoors, or hurt, her problem remained locked within her because she could not "tell" me in any comprehensible way what she wanted or needed. Joan cried and waved her arms haphazardly all about her in a vain attempt to express herself, and she and I grew more and more frustrated because we simply did not understand each other. The day abounded in crises which this situation created. For example, although Joan always loved playing outdoors, she could never "tell" me when she wanted to go out. She never brought me her coat, nor did she ever point specifically to the door to suggest what she wanted. Neither could she seem to understand what I was "telling" her when I brought her coat to her. Very often she struggled fiercely to thwart me as I dressed her without realizing that she was negating her own desires. Once outside, Joan relaxed immediately and smiled happily, thus indicating that she was now pleased. We would return for lunch, and after Joan had her nap, I would prepare to take her out again. Once more, we would become engaged in the same tussle as before because she could not recall the previous experience. Each activity seemed frighteningly new to her each and every time it occurred.

Joan could not associate her need with the means of gratifying it even if the means of doing so were right before her. For instance, if she was thirsty, and there was a container of milk on the table, she could not point to it, touch it, take it, or convey in any way, her desire for a drink. She would only cry, and fling her arms about in her usual manner. The burden of interpretation rested solely with me. By trial and error, I sometimes arrived at the correct answer. If she drank from the glass I offered to her, I knew that I was right. If I guessed incorrectly, she threw the glass on the floor, and continued crying until either I reached the correct conclusion or she was distracted by some other need.

On the verbal level, Joan showed no comprehension of words. Even those in common use baffled her completely. Words like mommie, daddy, hi, bye, yes, no, baby, toy, cookie, milk, play, ride, or car seemed to mean nothing to her. She did not even know her own name.

We were certain that Joan could hear. She had always responded to noises. Loud, strange ones alarmed her and made her cry. Familiar ones like the door bell or the vacuum cleaner running made her glance up. The one serious omission was her lack of response to speech sounds. She appeared oblivious to her brothers' chatter, my talking, the radio, or the record player. We were further puzzled by the fact that she never developed any substitute language of her own. Aside from crying and laughing, she made few, if any, sounds.

We wondered whether this delayed development could be a family trait because our two boys had been late walkers (seventeen and twenty months, respectively), and late talkers. They had not spoken until the age of two, and were not really articulate until the age of three. We quickly dismissed this theory because one significant difference between our sons and our daughter negated it. The boys had understood and responded to language from earliest infancy, and had used pantomine skillfully to express themselves before they could speak. They could communicate.

We could not deny that the difference between Joan and her contemporaries was becoming more obvious each day. However, we did nothing about it except to continue to try to stimulate speech by reading to her, talking to her, playing records, and having play and other experiences with her. We were content to let her develop at her own pace. We had always felt that one of the ways to achieve a healthy personality was to avoid pressure of any kind on our children to perform according to the classic text book presentation. Even though Joan showed little sign of language comprehension, we remained relatively relaxed about the situation because she showed good intelligence and steady progress in the manual, concrete areas of living. She continued to demonstrate competence in handling complex toys and gadgets.

As long as there was growth, we felt that we could be patient. As far as we knew, there was no physical reason why Joan could not communicate. We thought it was merely a question of time before language development would occur. We were confident that as soon as this was achieved, there would be an improvement in Joan's behavior. It was slowly becoming more and more apparent to us that her irrational behavior was not based on deliberate defiance or willful malice. Her destructive responses were beyond her control because all disciplines were beyond her comprehension.

Thus, until this point, we had essentially denied to ourselves the existence of a problem serious enough to require seeking help for it. We had built up a fine rationale for explaining Joan to ourselves. Her prematurity, her individual rate of development, a probable immaturity of her nervous system, and frustration based on lack of language were some of the alibis that lulled us into inactivity.

In addition, another factor existed that carried great weight with us. Our pediatrician, who had known Joan from birth, was fully confident that Joan's development was normal. On routine visits to him, he always reassured us when we raised questions that we somehow could not reason away. When he observed Joan briefly in his office and in our home, he noted her bright eyes, her quick, searching movements, her dexterity, and her ready smiles. He appeared unconcerned about her lack of speech and her inability to relate to people. He felt that she had speech comprehension (a faulty observation on his part, we thought) and dismissed as exaggeration our accounts of her behavior. Since we considered him to be a competent physician, we trusted his opinion that Joan was actually bright and alert, and his conclusion that she was developing normally. His explanation for her delayed language responses was that she was merely proceeding at a different rate from that of her contemporaries. He felt that this was based on her marked prematurity. We welcomed his assurances. We wanted to believe him. I think that this was one of the most important reasons we did not become alarmed and did not seek further opinions.

At our request, our pediatrician prescribed tranquilizers once or twice to help reduce Joan's hyperactivity, but she did not respond to them.

We plodded on with the eager anticipation and fervent hope that each new day would release the words we hoped lay merely dormant within Joan. This expectation remained unfulfilled. The days continued to be long and miserable. They varied only in that some were more intolerable than others. None were good.

Chapter 6

PROGRESS AND HELP

Finally, when joan was just about three and one-half years old, subtle changes began to take place in her orientation. She began to show some signs of emerging from her withdrawal. For the first time, gestures began to have some meaning for her. As the weeks passed, she became more and more adept at interpreting my gestures. However, she was still not able to use motions herself to transmit her wants to me. This was a serious handicap because it meant that Joan still had no means of communicating her needs.

At the same time that Joan began to respond to gestures, she began to react to speech sounds. At first, the nature of the response was unclear to us. When we spoke to her, we would observe her pausing momentarily in her wild, seemingly purposeless activity. Although she would seem to be listening, we soon discovered that she was actually looking for gestural clues accompanying the sounds. Without the motions, she was uncomprehending. The sounds seemed to serve as a signal to Joan to take note of the gestures. When she responded appropriately, one could easily conclude that Joan was acting upon the words. This was decidedly not so.

Then, some language progress began to take place. After several weeks, Joan began to respond to a few nouns, but she still could not speak at all. The deluge of words we had expected was not forthcoming.

We were not feeling as complacent as we had felt heretofore, so we arranged for a diagnostic consultation with a psychologist who used non-verbal tests. Joan was essentially uncooperative, tense, and uncomprehending. The tests, which lasted about an hour, gave inconclusive results. Although Joan was unable to understand the simplest directions, she handled the non-verbal test materials with some success. The fact that she had practically no speech or comprehension of speech proved to be a handicap for the examiner. She could give us no recommendations, but stated a "hunch" that Joan had normal intelligence.

Soon thereafter, an unexpected occurrence gave us the impetus to seek help in dealing with Joan. In April, when Joan was exactly three and one-half years old, our pediatrician died, and we went to another one. During the doctor's first routine examination of Joan in his office, he observed her carefully and immediately expressed concern about her unusually poor language responses. He told us that language must be integrated by the time a child is five or six years old, or it might never occur. His examination revealed no physical reason for her lack of communication.

We were grateful for the astuteness he demonstrated in recognizing the existence of a serious problem. However, we were alarmed by the urgency that he expressed, and upset by the thought that we might have already lost valuable time. We were also concerned about the prognosis.

The pediatrician recommended that we seek diagnosis and treatment without any further delay. He referred us to the head of a speech clinic in a nearby hospital where we made an appointment immediately.

We had our first interview with the speech therapist in June, nineteen hundred and fifty-six. He observed Joan and noted the marked inconsistencies in her responses: skill in non-verbal activities and practically no comprehension in verbal areas. We discussed the extent of Joan's extreme dependence upon us, her marked immaturity, her withdrawal, and her egocentricity. We questioned her lack of speech and her unrelatedness. The speech therapist gave us no diagnosis because he was puzzled by the clinical picture Joan presented. He acknowledged the existence of a serious language deficiency and a serious behavior problem. In the course of the discussion, he recommended therapy for Joan. He also outlined specific goals and suggested a program he felt should be established for her at the clinic. His plan was to see her twice a week for about half an hour each time in an attempt to establish a relationship with her and to stimulate speech. We accepted his judgment without question and felt very relieved that, at last, someone was going to make a directed effort to help Joan with what we now admitted was a problem too serious to resolve itself.

Since the nature of the problem was so obscure, we began to be concerned about whether the intelligence we felt Joan possessed could ever be expressed on a level consistent with what was to be expected of a normally developing child. The speech therapist reassured us, and expressed confidence that, in time, Joan would begin to relate to people and would speak. Since this was an atypical case, he admitted that he had few guide lines to use. However he was willing to use what skills and experience he possessed in an effort to help her. We felt somewhat encouraged, and cherished his warm, sincere, sympathetic approach to Joan and to us. Now we looked forward eagerly to September when the therapeutic sessions were scheduled to begin. I think we were expecting miracles to happen.

During the summer interval, Joan began to understand a few more common nouns that are frequently used. She attempted to speak. It was a taxing effort for her, and she seldom succeeded in saying more than a word or two at a time. Even though very few words had any meaning for her, she was now able to mimic and could repeat a few words after me. Her speech was monosyllabic and was very poorly enunciated. She spoke in a monotone. Many speech sounds were totally absent. It was extremely difficult to understand her.

In September, the formal therapy sessions at the clinic began. Joan was given a physical examination which included neurological tests (the results were negative), a hearing test (the results were inconclusive because she was frightened and uncooperative, but they demonstrated that she had hearing), and Joan and I had a joint interview with a psychiatrist. The result of the psychiatric evaluation was a recommendation that I receive intensive therapy. I rejected this suggestion, because I could not understand the reason for it and proceeded to concentrate on what seemed to me to be the problem, namely Joan's difficulty with language.

Joan was now almost four years old. A program was being launched at the clinic to help our child develop her potential. We knew that her native intelligence would remain unharnessed, and she would continue to function poorly if she did not begin to relate to people and did not learn how to communicate. Her self centeredness was incapacitating because it kept her locked within herself, unheeding and unaware of anyone or anything about her. Therapy at the clinic was aimed primarily at helping Joan establish relationships. The speech therapist felt that communication on a non-verbal level had to be accomplished before Joan could go on to learn words.

Since Joan's ability to recall the past was so poor, she greeted each session as a brand new experience. Tense and withdrawn, she clung to me and forced me to stay with her through the session. Inside the therapy room, she occupied herself with the physical tools she found there like the sink, pop guns, balls, building blocks, cars, and trucks. These were concrete, manipulative, non-verbal activities at which she was adept. The cause and effect mechanism here was readily apparent to her. She balked, at first, at any structured work experience with more abstract tools such as books and words. However, after several weeks of persistent effort on the part of the therapist, Joan began to accept some work disciplines, and the play period became correspondingly shorter.

When the therapist finally established this measure of contact with Joan, we felt very encouraged. After a while, more and more of the period was devoted to learning experiences, and finally, the play period was reduced to a minimum. As the relationship between them became more meaningful, Joan could let go of me a little. She would allow me to step out of the therapy room. At times, I could hear laughter coming from the room because she was enjoying something with the therapist. With each successive contact, Joan was recalling a little more of her previous experience. After several weeks, she let herself be enticed into the therapy room without me.

I had a regular weekly contact with the staff social worker in order to discuss Joan's behavior at the clinic and at home. These sessions provided me with information about Joan's progress, and gave me the opportunity to explore methods of dealing with her.

At the same time as progress was being made at the clinic, we noted progress at home. Some time between the ages of four and four and one-half, Joan began to use the toilet. She had complete control during the day from the time she started. However, she continued to wet her bed at night.

I had proceeded with Joan's toilet training in the same way that I had handled it with the boys, who had responded when they were about three and one-half years old. They were told the function of the toilet. Aside from this, I made no special effort to train them.

Further progress of a more significant nature was taking place. The greater relatedness that Joan was exhibiting with the speech therapist was now reflected in her behavior at home. Joan was beginning to relate to me and to the family. She now seemed to understand that my husband and I were special people: Mommie and Daddy. However, she was still very confused about our separate roles.

There was also progress in her relationships with children. Joan had always loved having children play near her, and now she expressed her delight by running to meet them when they came to play in our backyard playground or in our home. She seemed happy and comfortable as they played beside her. Her behavior had improved to the extent that she no longer expressed hostility towards them, and they did not need to run away.

We began to allow ourselves to hope that she might eventually develop into a healthy normal human being. The first indication I had that there was a possibility that a feeling person was emerging from this self centered individual was the day I stopped off to deliver some school material to a friend. Joan was about four years and two months old. This friend gave Joan a naked doll that her own daughter had discarded. Dolls had, up until this point, seemed to have little meaning for Joan. She usually hurled, smashed, or dragged them around. However, now, she took the doll with a pleased expression on her face, and held it tightly all the way downstairs. As we prepared to step outside into the cold winter air, Joan stepped back, clutched the doll tightly to her, and said, "Baby cold." She would not come out of the hallway until I had tucked the doll snugly into her coat. Holding it this way, she carried it home. This doll became a favorite toy. We got clothes for her, and Joan enjoyed dressing and undressing her.

This was a memorable event. It demonstrated to us that Joan was beginning to understand something outside of herself. Her world was enlarging a little. She was showing that she was capable of expressing feeling. She was beginning to recognize relationships between ideas.

Generally, there was improvement in Joan's overt behavior. There were far fewer tantrums, and there was considerably less hyperactivity and aggression. However, Joan's ability to integrate ideas and understand the nature of relationship was still very limited. As a result, the day to day care of Joan remained extremely difficult. Her dependence upon me increased to the point where we were virtually inseparable. She made many unreasonable demands like expecting us to restore a totally destroyed toy, or give her a dangerous gadget to play with. She did not understand the implications of her requests. Joan was still largely unresponsive to most controls. She continued to be bewildered most of the time because she did not yet recognize the routines in her day. This made her tense, fretful, and demanding.

The trips to the speech clinic were hazardous experiences. I found it necessary, for our mutual safety, to put Joan in a little seat which was firmly anchored down in the back of the car at the side away from the driver's seat. She was strapped in. This was something Joan did herself after watching me do it a few times. It was necessary to do this because she poked me if she could reach me. This was too risky while driving.

I always gave her something to play with that might interest her, and something to eat to keep her occupied and relaxed. She usually hurled the play thing somewhere in the car, and quickly ate the cracker or cookie. The entire half hour trip was full of cries of frustration, protest against being confined, demands for attention, and dangerous distractions. Joan simply could not understand what was diverting my attention from her, and why I was not speaking to her. I could not calm her down or control her behavior. Many times, I despaired of making the trip safely.

On the other hand, there was some encouraging progress in the language area, and therein lay our hopes for better understanding between Joan and us. Speech was definitely emerging at last. The efforts Joan was making to speak were both heartening and pathetic. Since early infancy, I had always said, "Good night, Joan" as I tucked her into bed each night. Now that she was becoming aware of speech, she tried to mimic me. However, for many weeks, she could only say "good," or "night," or "Mommie." This seemed to represent the maximum effort that she could make. She tried and tried but could do no more. Finally, she began to link two words like "good Mommie," or "night Mommie," or "good night," but that was all. The words actually seemed to have little or no meaning for her.

Once words were learned, Joan had a long hard haul before she could learn how to use them. Each labored step she took highlighted dramatically how steep the climb was and how long the road.

With the insights I had achieved into the scope of Joan's language problems, I felt that further work at home might accelerate the learning process. When I discussed this with the speech therapist, he suggested that I not teach her. However, I felt very strongly that it was important to give Joan as much help as she could use. Therefore, from the very beginning of my clinic contact, I borrowed the therapist's techniques and methods which I had an opportunity to observe while being held "captive" in the therapy room by Joan and maintained a daily structured teaching routine with her.

At the clinic, the speech therapist used a variety of educational materials. One of his tools was an assortment of lotto cards. Joan started by matching like objects and could do this skillfully long before she knew the function of the objects or the language connected with them. He asked her to identify, in books and in lotto games, objects in common use. When a small base line of language was established, the speech therapist proceeded to teach her important concepts, building more and more vocabulary as he went along. Joan finally began to learn that certain things belong together like shoe and foot, window and house, boat and water, milk and cup, and so on. Eventually, she moved on to the learning of more complex concepts like what the parts of a unit were. She learned that a car has four wheels, a spoon has a handle, a building has a roof, a person has two arms, two legs, a head, and so on.

Joan's figure drawings showed marked disorientation. Parts of the body were missing, misplaced, or grotesquely proportioned. She could not yet recognize her counterpart in pictures or play models. For her, there was as yet, no connection between the toy house that she played with and the house in which she lived. She had little understanding of her environment or of the people in it.

At home, from the very outset, Joan responded eagerly and willingly to the teaching program I established, and I was able to enforce some work disciplines successfully. I was tremendously encouraged by her responses. Several factors were beginning to operate in our favor. Joan was finally beginning to understand the concept of approval and disapproval. She enjoyed the undivided attention I gave her. She liked the materials I was using. However, her ability to concentrate was very limited, and I had to bring her back into focus all the time. As soon as I saw a far away lost look in her eyes, I faced her towards me, and with her hands firmly clasped in mine, I literally forced her to attend to me. I used all of my will and strength to hold her. She proved to be so elusive, that I could only keep her attention for a few minutes at a time. I was actually making tremendous demands of her.

It was imperative to build a core of vocabulary and *The Golden Dictionary,** a Giant Golden Book, was invaluable for this purpose. I would open it to a picture of a common object like table. We would look at the picture, say the word, relate it to the table at which we sat, and find its counterparts all through the house and in books and magazines. Joan was not able to make the connection independently between the table we were using and the table in the next room. She did not understand that tables have different uses and that they can have different appearances. She could link two identical spoons or two identical pencils, but if there was a variation in color, size, or design, she was bewildered.

Initially, we could use only a group of two or three words a day, some old and some new. As time went on, we accelerated our speed. Joan could recognize and understand a new word approximately two weeks to a month after she started learning it. While she was learning a new word, its meaning and use eluded her from one minute to the next. Her mind ressembled a field of quicksand. The word impressions disappeared constantly and only by continued repetition was she finally able to retain it. After a word seemed learned, we had to use it constantly or its meaning would disappear entirely. When this happened, we had to start the process over again. At first, the relearning involved as much time and effort as it took to teach her the words originally. Joan, at that time, never independently extracted concepts or words from her environment. Every single word and idea that she possessed was etched into her mind by the specific teaching devices we used.

Along with *The Golden Dictionary,* I used jig saw puzzles to aid her in her conceptual understanding. We worked on simple three piece puzzles at first and more complex ones later on. In the beginning, these merely proved to be exercises in manual dexterity because Joan quickly perceived the differences in the shapes of the pieces. Therefore, she could assemble them competently. What Joan did not realize was that she was constructing a unit that had meaning such as a rabbit, a wagon, or a house. As she became better integrated, her work with the puzzles became meaningful because they served to help build up her conceptual awareness. Soon Joan put the chimney on top of the roof, the wheels on the wagon, and the carrot in the bunny's paw

---

*For a complete listing of educational materials see appendix.

because she was beginning to see that these things went together to form a whole.

In Joan's learning, I noted a pattern that I continued to recognize, with slight variations, for years to come. There would be a small amount of progress for several weeks. This would be followed by a period of no learning that sometimes lasted just as long. Then serious regressions would occur. During this time, Joan would often revert to a very low level of behavior and language understanding. It would seem to me, at these points, that she was making no progress at all. Then, for no discernible reason, there would be a marvelous upsurge of learning. Old material would be recalled and new material would be learned at a faster rate. Perhaps, consolidation of what had been learned, was taking place. In any event, the total picture definitely showed progress. During the early years, the serious regressions, which lasted from two weeks to two months, occurred about four or five times a year. Minor regressions, lasting about a week or two, occurred quite often. As Joan progressed in her development, the number and duration of the regressions decreased.

I could never associate these regressions and spurts of learning with anything in Joan's physical or emotional environment. She was always extremely robust and healthy. There were no changes in her day to day living that could explain what was happening to her. I was still trying to provide her with as secure and stable an environment as I possibly could. While her progress seemed imperceptible at first, she was beginning to move at an accelerated pace. The picture often looked bleak, but we could see improvement when we looked back over a period of months.

However, we were conscious of the swift passage of time, and ever mindful of what our pediatrician had told us about the importance of establishing language as early as possible. Joan's impairment was still extremely severe. When my husband and I examined the advances she had made, we realized that, at the age of four years and four months, Joan had made just a fraction of the progress she needed to make in order to function adequately. The six month barrage of work at the clinic and at home had broken the stalemate, but she was, at best, moving at only a snail's pace. In our desire for a greater understanding of Joan's problems and increased help for Joan, we looked for someone who could give us the insights we needed. This pursuit led us, to our great good fortune, to a professional contact that represented a major turning point in Joan's life.

JOAN AT THE AGE OF FOUR YEARS AND SIX MONTHS

Chapter 7

WE FORGE AHEAD

In february, nineteen hundred and fifty-eight, when Joan was four years and four months old, and had attended the speech clinic for six months, we learned from a friend, who is a physician, about studies being done on premature infants at Columbia Presbyterian Medical Center in New York. There we were referred to Mrs. Shulamith Kastein, a speech pathologist.

In our first contact, the speech pathologist conducted a lengthy testing session with Joan, and interviewed my husband and myself. Her skill was evident in her calm, confident, and persuasive handling of our little girl. However, throughout the session, Joan was remote and unrelated. Her span of attention was very brief. She tired easily and was generally tense. Nevertheless, she tried to cooperate.

From the very outset, my husband and I felt genuine rapport with the speech pathologist because she included us so fully in her interpretation of Joan and her problem. Apparently, the way she understood her professional role was to regard all of those involved with Joan as a team embarking on an important investigation. I cannot emphasize too strongly the significance of this point of view to both my husband and myself. It prevailed throughout our relationship and contributed importantly to the events that followed. Helping Joan was our mutual goal in every sense.

This initial consultation marked a breakthrough in what was, thus far, a largely unresolved situation. The speech pathologist was the first professional person who recognized and understood the specific nature of Joan's problem. She diagnosed it as a dysfunction of the central nervous system and a receptive language disorder. She acknowledged the possibility that a hearing defect might also exist. However, she felt as we did, that if it existed, it could not be a significant one. Joan obviously could hear speech sounds.

Of even greater importance to us than the diagnosis was the fact that the speech pathologist knew what procedure to follow in order to deal with the problem. Since she felt that Joan had good intelligence,

53

she was confident that the condition could be corrected. Over and over again, she stressed the importance of giving Joan maximum help without any delay. There was no question about the urgency in her manner as she explained that if language was not developed in Joan before she was six or seven years old, she might be essentially handicapped for life.

We now wanted to know who could provide the help Joan needed. Although the speech pathologist acknowledged the importance of the work being done at the speech clinic, she considered it insufficient in terms of the amount of time Joan spent there. We seemed now to be faced with a problem of how to get more help for her. The speech pathologist had a suggestion. After establishing, as well as she could, that my attitude toward Joan was positive, she recommended that I undertake the responsibility for helping Joan myself. Her proposal surprised me. I certainly had a most ardent desire to do everything possible to help our little daughter, but I had no specific training, experience, or knowledge that could qualify me to follow the kind of habilitative program the speech pathologist was suggesting. This raised doubts and questions I could not ignore. In response, the speech pathologist pointed out that we actually had no choice. She expressed confidence in me and pledged her full support.

This was immediately forthcoming in a description of methods for stimulating speech, and an outline of the concepts that needed to be developed and integrated. The speech pathologist recommended that I acquaint myself with the Montessori Method for sense training. She stressed the importance of exposing Joan to a great deal of experiential learning. My work with Joan was to supplement the therapy she was receiving at the speech clinic. The speech pathologist and the speech therapist were to maintain a professional contact with each other in order to discuss Joan's progress and plan her therapeutic program.

During this first conference that my husband and I had with the speech pathologist, we all acknowledged the importance of weaning Joan away from me. She was still far too dependent. To deal with this aspect of her problem, the speech pathologist recommended a nursery school experience for Joan as soon as possible.

Joan was not quite ready yet for the group situation, but by April, we felt that the time was ripe for enrolling her in a nursery school. We could consider taking this step now because of the advances Joan had made. She was relating a little better to people and was accepting some limits. She was struggling a little less with her environment because she was slightly more aware of its structure. With this small degree of improvement in her behavior, we felt, for the first time, that not only could Joan function within a group, but could perhaps derive some benefit from it. She still, of course, had a multitude of unresolved problems that required specialized training, but we hoped that daily contact with her peers might, at least, help her in one major area. We wanted to see her grow more independent, and hoped that increased relationships with people outside the home might help break the Gordian knot that bound Joan and me together so tightly.

I tried to prepare Joan for nursery school, but made little, if any, impression upon her. She went willingly with me because we were inseparable, but would only stay if I remained with her. After allowing her a few days to adjust to the strange surroundings and new relationships, I made several attempts to leave but was unsuccessful. Weeks passed and I still had to attend school with her. Perhaps I could have succeeded in forcibly wrenching myself from her side, but I believe the consequences could have been serious. When I noted her extreme agitation as I moved about the room, momentarily out of her line of vision, I made the decision to stay as long as she needed me. Our hope, after all, was to have a well-adjusted child, not just an independent one.

The teacher acknowledged Joan's need for me, and fully sanctioned my stay in the classroom. I tried to be unobtrusive, and directed Joan back to her teacher whenever she came to me for help. In time, she began to relate more and more to the teacher. She also began to realize that my role in school was different than my role at home.

Joan was now being provided with typical childhood social experiences. Although she seemed not to react to the children's speech and was unable to communicate with them verbally, she obviously enjoyed being near them. It was good to see her respect the children's rights and possessions, and strongly defend her own rights. Joan seemed to understand some of the limits the teacher imposed on the class. She became a bona fide member of the group because she conformed well to its structure and disciplines. Observing her, I knew that this was not based on a comprehension of what was happening all about her. She could conform, largely because she was alert and watchful, and could imitate the actions of the others. For instance, when the teacher asked her to get ready to go outside, she did not seem to understand the request. However, when she saw the other children line up, she quickly joined the group fully dressed and ready. It seemed to those who observed her, that she was responding to the teacher's spoken directions, but I knew that it was her visual astuteness that enabled her to perform efficiently here.

Joan was extremely active and participated happily in most of the physical aspects of the school program. However, when it came to activities involving language, she was restless and unheeding. During story time, for example, she spread her blanket and lay down obediently with the other children. However, she could not listen to the story. She spent the time turning the pages of a book, straightening her blanket, and wriggling on the floor. She resented being confined. While many of the children were bored and restless, they, at least, heard and understood the story. Joan seemed not to grasp anything.

Even though Joan was using the school experience in a limited way, we felt that it was definitely benefiting her. School was providing her with the opportunity to have relationships with her contemporaries. It was also exposing her to different disciplines, and giving her an opportunity to explore varied activities. She was apparently using the nursery school materials to some advantage and enjoying them too.

However, it was evident that the main impetus to her language development would have to emanate from the home program. With the specific guides that the speech pathologist had given me, I had clarity for the first time about my objectives. Our work now had direction. Certainly, much of it was a continuation of what we had been doing, but knowing what to aim for and what had to be achieved made all the difference in the world.

In addition to the methods that the speech pathologist outlined, I used as many other devices as I could find. These included aids from the staff at the speech clinic, suggestions from the teachers at school, material from the school psychologist, books from the library and the shelves of the local book stores, and my own resources and knowledge. Joan and I were involved in a dynamic process, and anything that worked was valid.

Since Joan attended school each morning, we established our formal work sessions in the afternoon. They lasted, depending upon her responses, from one half hour to two hours each day in one long period or in several brief ones. Gradually, I increased these learning periods to three or four hours per day. When Joan tired, we rested at our work table, singing, clapping our hands, or playing with a toy. Then we resumed our work. We shortened this schedule only when I felt that we had already achieved the maximum for the day, and Joan could not go on any longer. Actually, the teaching process began the moment that Joan awoke in the morning and continued until she went to sleep. It was a round-the-clock procedure. I used every opportunity that presented itself to teach words, to reinforce them, and to help her to develop language.

It was apparent that further improvement in Joan's behavior was dependent upon an increased understanding of concepts and words. For instance, she still had tremendous difficulty in comprehending how cause and effect operated except on the most concrete level. Joan became frustrated and frenzied if there was even the smallest delay in complying with her wishes. She simply could not understand why I did not answer her while I was brushing my teeth, or why I could not find her ball while I was in the bathtub. This put enormous pressure on both of us.

To help Joan understand the concept of time, an area of hopeless confusion, I tried to put abstract experiences into concrete terms wherever possible. Those that I could not translate just continued to create problems for her.

We toasted bread under the broiler, so that Joan could see it get brown, and we watched water get hot and begin to boil. Joan poured milk or water into a glass to learn how it gets there. I hoped that she would learn from these experiences that it takes time for bread to brown, for water to boil, and for a glass to fill up.

When Joan saw me preparing foods like hamburgers or scrambled eggs, she wanted to have them immediately. I let her sample raw eggs and raw meat, and she found them distasteful. We then cooked these foods to show how heat changed and improved their taste, texture, color and smell. This she could comprehend, but it was very difficult for her to grasp the fact that it took time to convert food from an unpalatable to a palatable state. We repeated these experiences over and over again until she could understand this concept. Then, it took months before she knew enough words like later, soon, not yet, in a few minutes, when it is done, and so on, to translate this new found understanding into greater self control.

In teaching Joan, I used many books, games, and materials. The most useful were *The Golden Dictionary*, puzzles, lotto games, finger paints, drawing and coloring books, story books, records, and common everyday objects such as buttons, blocks, fabrics, spools of thread, coins, boxes, household utensils, pots, pans, and many others. Following the speech pathologist's suggestion, Joan and I increased the number of experiences we had been having together. We washed clothes, fixed closets and drawers, went to the post office, the pet store, and department stores. We shopped and handled money. We visited the fire house, the zoo, the circus, and an animal farm. We visited friends. Although we had had most of these experiences before, they had always been essentially meaningless to Joan. However, now that they were coupled in our daily work sessions with a specific learning process, these abstract words and concepts finally began to take on some small meaning. For example, before and after seeing animals in the zoo, we looked at pictures of them in books. I read animal stories to her such as *The Animals of Farmer Jones, Baby Animals,* and others. We made animal noises, and I tried to teach her the anatomical differences between animals and humans, as well as the vocabulary dealing with animals. The words and ideas were all new and difficult for Joan to comprehend and learning was scarcely perceptible at first. However, the teaching processes were flexible, and I tried new and different ways of reaching her. Constant repetition was necessary because Joan's memory was so poor. Therefore, it literally took months of word training before enough vocabulary was established for these experiences to have any real meaning. We kept repeating the same outings, extracting a little more from them each time. Very slowly, one by one, these experiences became integrated and Joan began to recognize them as part of her life. When this happened, she could begin to use them.

As our work continued, I used books and records differently because I was understanding the nature of Joan's difficulties better. I had long before discovered that simply reading a story to Joan had little or no value, so my approach had to be modified. Using the very simplest books, I taught her the vocabulary first, and together we acted out the story line. Joan merely mimicked me at the outset because she was just barely aware of the function of words in expressing an idea. She withdrew constantly from our activity, and responded only when the story was concrete. She could not deal with a story that began, "The little boy *went into* the forest *because he wanted to find some* birds." This was too abstract. However, the story that related, "The boy had a balloon. He broke it." was somewhat easier for her to grasp because we could dramatize it, and she could see the action. We confined ourselves to the latter type of story for the time being.

I also found it helpful to construct my own stories using simple vocabulary, short sentences, and concrete ideas that she had already mastered. I drew upon experiences and situations that were familiar to Joan for my story line. I worked with only one sentence at a time, and moved on only when she had absorbed it fairly well.

I used action records designed for the one to two year old child. They were the Tom Glaser Pram records, *Where Are Your Eyes, Bye Bye, Big and Little, Sleepy Time, Toys,* and *Nice.* They employed simple basic vocabulary, and common experiences inherent in everyday living. Joan was charmed by the music, but was confused by the words. Although she had been exposed to these records constantly from early infancy, she had never really "heard" them. Now she seemed ready to learn the words, and to understand the ideas they expressed. When we started working intensively on the records, we translated them as well as possible into concrete terms, but initially, she was only able to imitate me. Gradually, after several weeks of work, Joan began to show a fair degree of understanding of the words.

I started to use the Montessori method of sense training in order to assist Joan in the development of her senses. The Montessori Material was not available in this country at this time, so I collected my own materials. To help Joan learn about color, I used spools of thread and pieces of fabric. After she learned to identify colors, we worked on shades of color to develop her awareness of color more fully. To make her aware of different tastes, I gave her sweet, sour, and salty foods. Her sense of smell was stimulated by flowers, burning matches, a cake baking, gasoline, and so on. To develop her sense of proportion, I used the following: for size; coins, blocks, and books—for length; wooden dowels, pieces of string, strips of paper, and people's height. I used boxes in which I distributed different numbers of coins to teach Joan about weight. She learned first the concept of light and heavy, and then went on to learn about gradations in weight. Joan learned about the thickness of objects by comparing different books, cereal boxes, and so on. For the development of her tactile sense, I found different textures of fabric and surfaces of the furniture and household objects useful. She touched water of varying temperatures to develop a thermal sense. Most of these experiences delighted Joan. We had excellent success because Joan only had to see, touch, smell, and taste in order to learn. There were few abstractions here. The terminology, of course, proved to be elusive because of her poor memory. She required much drill, but did learn the descriptive words after several months.

As we worked, the very serious lacks in Joan's total orientation were becoming more and more obvious to me. The more we struggled, the better I understood how incredible her separation from the world was. I sometimes wondered if our goals were attainable because the number of words she needed to learn and the concepts she needed to understand seemed infinite in number. The process was so slow that there were times when I felt that Joan was actually going backwards, that she was unreachable, and that her mind was like a sieve that would hold nothing. When I despaired, my husband gave me tremendous support, and was able to show me that we were indeed moving ahead.

As for Joan's nursery school experience, the session ended in May. Joan had attended for six weeks. In our final conference at the school, the director reported that Joan had been making good progress, and he recommended that she be advanced to the kindergarten group in September. This tremendous vote of confidence in Joan amazed and delighted us. We scheduled a second meeting with the speech pathologist in order to evaluate Joan's general progress and to consider this challenging suggestion.

Chapter 8

THE SPECIFIC NATURE OF SOME OF
JOAN'S LANGUAGE DIFFICULTIES

At this may conference, the speech pathologist tested Joan and found that she had indeed made progress in the intervening three months. She readjusted the training program to meet Joan's changing needs and gave me further concrete suggestions. I could not have advanced without this specific help. As far as kindergarten was concerned, the speech pathologist welcomed the proposal and recommended that we proceed with it in the Fall. Her objective evaluation of the situation was invaluable.

However, her role had even greater dimension. The scope of Joan's needs was gigantic, her progress was very slow, the program was ambitious, and I again questioned my ability to implement it. I expressed all this to the speech pathologist. Based on what had been accomplished thus far, she strongly affirmed the validity of my role in helping Joan. She scarcely admitted to us any doubts about the successful completion of this project.

Her tremendous clarity and her confidence in Joan and in me gave me the impetus to go on. Its immediate effect was to lift the gloom. Its long range effect was to increase my personal strength and lead me on to more creative approaches to Joan's problems.

As of June, nineteen hundred and fifty-eight, when Joan was four years and eight months old, we estimated that she could use approximately one hundred words, and she could understand about fifty more. These were simple concrete nouns such as car, milk, toy, candy, balloon, ball, pencil, book, and so on. I was able to teach her these words with relative ease because I could show her the object and then name it for her. Eventually, after much repetition, she retained it. It still took her from two weeks to a month to learn a word well enough so that she could use it. This learning had to be reinforced constantly because her memory had hardly improved at all. We worked with one word at a time adding new ones as soon as it was possible.

61

Teaching Joan the meanings of verbs proved to be a much more arduous task than teaching her nouns. Those verbs that I could demonstrate like sit, throw, ride, dress, eat, sing, jump, walk, and so on, she learned much more readily than the more abstract ones. For instance, if I said, "I *eat* a cookie," I could show her what *eat* meant, but if I said, "I *want* a cookie," I had no concrete way of explaining the abstract verb *want* to her. Holding out my hand to demonstrate the verb taught her the meaning only within one context. When I used the verb in other contexts like, "I *want* to brush my hair," "Do you *want* to go out?" or "Do you *want* a drink of milk?" she was unable to understand and respond.

Words like *pick up* confused her endlessly. I showed her the action repeatedly and used the verb only with nouns she had already mastered. However, when I directed her to *pick up* the pencil, she only knew that she had to do something with the pencil. Consequently, she might throw it, roll it, drop it on the floor, bring it upstairs, hand it to me, or pick it up. The action was unrelated except by accident to what I had said. Even after she had learned to respond to the phrase "*pick up* the pencil," she could not apply this learning to other phrases such as, "*pick up* the spoon," "*pick up* the book," "*pick up* the toy," and so on. She simply could not understand the words within varying contexts. Furthermore, she responded to each phrase as if it was one word because she did not understand its components yet.

For some weeks and months, Joan continued to respond in a very limited way to the words she had learned because she continued to understand them only within very specific contexts. For example, we went for a ride in the car almost every day. As soon as I said, "We are going for a *ride* in the car," Joan would rush into the car. However, if I said that she could *ride* in her wagon, or *ride* on her rocking horse, or give her doll a *ride* in the carriage, she became confused, and rushed towards the car, or pointed to the carriage, the horse or the wagon. Here again, she seemed to hear and understand the entire phrase as if it was one word. It took her a long time to grasp the meaning of the verb *to ride* well enough so that she could recognize it and interpret it within other contexts.

Similarly, when Joan learned the verb *to drink,* she learned it and understood it only in connection with milk even though I varied the context within which I used it. Therefore, she had to learn separately the meanings of the phrases *"drinking* water," *"drinking* juice," and *"drinking* soda." In her day-to-day living, Joan functioned most competently and intelligently, knowing well what to do with a ball, a cookie, juice, a toy car, swings, spoons, and so on. It was only when she had to respond to language that she was baffled.

In order to teach Joan the meanings of abstract words and how to use them within different contexts, I demonstrated them to her in a variety of ways. Words like *up* and *down* were particularly elusive. Therefore, for a seemingly endless procession of hours, we stood *up* and sat *down,* picked *up* and put *down* a toy, raised our arms *up* and put them *down,* pushed *up* a window and pulled it *down,* threw a pencil *up* and watched it fall *down,* pulled a zipper *up* and then pulled it *down,* tossed a ball *up* and watched it fall *down,* and so on. Even when Joan learned what *up* and *down* meant, she confused the meanings of the two words, and used them interchangeably. If she was holding a ball, and I asked her to throw it *up* in the air, half the time she would bounce it *down.*

We repeated this same process with other groups of extremely troublesome words like *yes* and *no, give* and *take, open* and *close, come* and *go, eat* and *drink, on* and *off, before* and *after, now* and *later, ask* and *tell, sit* and *stand,* and so on. Here again, these were all commonplace words involving familiar activities that Joan performed competently each day without any hesitation or confusion. It was only the language connected with these activities that was incomprehensible to her.

I reached an impasse that seemed almost insurmountable when I tried to teach Joan words that defied demonstration. A word like *hurt* was completely intangible. I could not explain it in any way that made sense to her because her knowledge of words was so limited. At this level, a word meant practically nothing to her unless she could see, touch, taste, or smell what it was trying to describe. Other words besides *hurt* that were particularly difficult for Joan to learn were *look, see, listen, think,* and so on. However, with continuous hard work, we did advance, and in spite of all these difficulties a basic vocabulary of both concrete and abstract words was slowly being built up.

Unfortunately, this was not nearly enough. Even with an expanding vocabulary, Joan was not a comprehending person in any real sense of the word. Her limited conceptual awareness prevented her from communicating on anything but the simplest level. It was important for me to focus as much attention as possible on increasing her conceptual understanding. To accomplish this, I had to be certain first that Joan knew the specific vocabulary used to express the concepts I was trying to teach her. Then, I had to use every conceivable device I knew of or could develop in order to make her understand them.

I would say that it took approximately one month to establish the meaning of a simple concept. Only then was it well enough integrated for her to use it. We worked on two or three at a time in our regular work sessions, but we were involved, of necessity, in a continuous process of teaching and learning throughout the day. This was the only way we could hope to make the progress that needed to be made in order to bring Joan anywhere near the level of her contemporaries.

Chapter 9

MORE ABOUT THE METHOD

THE MATERIALS I USED were essentially the same ones that I had been using all along, but my utilization of them varied to meet Joan's changing needs. It was a very dynamic process because my direction was largely dictated by Joan's specific needs as they presented themselves. Thus, when it became apparent that Joan did not have the foggiest notion about the function of a house, even though she could identify it and name it, my focus had to be turned towards helping her to integrate this concept. All of her information was fragmentary and unrelated because she was as yet unable to structure it. In this particular case, Joan had to learn about a house as a place for people to live in, work in, and play in. I tried to teach her about the different rooms, their uses, their furnishings, and the different people who lived in it. We drew pictures of various kinds of houses using *My Own Little House*, a step by step drawing of a house, as a guide. We used a large play model of a house, and arranged toy furniture and toy people in each room. In this way, Joan began to learn where things belonged and why they belonged there. She began to understand the functions of the various rooms, and who the occupants were. When I scattered the play furniture, she would attempt to arrange it in the proper rooms. Bit by bit, Joan learned how to do this well. We repeated this kind of play many, many times over the months. Eventually, Joan was able to tell me without visual aids where different articles of furniture belonged, and what the functions of the various rooms were.

However, even when these ideas were seemingly well established, Joan was not able to go on to understand a related concept. If we talked of schools, factories, banks, or stores, she could not make the connection between these buildings and the house she had learned about because she did not see the relationship between them. She did not recognize them as other kinds of houses with some similarities such as walls, roofs, doors, and windows; and some differences in size, shape, and function. Therefore, each structure had to be studied independently and thoroughly.

65

It was important to help Joan recognize the relationship between like objects that were dissimilar in some respects. It was also important to help her understand her own everyday experiences. To accomplish this, I began to use *The Golden Dictionary* in a special way. Turning to any page at random, I would ask Joan to show me all the things she could play with, the foods we eat, objects that move, what we find in a house, what girls wear, what boys wear, what can fly, pictures of daytime, pictures of nighttime, and so on. Her very poor responses, at first, demonstrated how limited her understanding was. She knew only those words and recognized those concepts that we had specifically worked on. However, the time we spent on this each day yielded results in that it gradually increased her vocabulary and improved her responses. It was valuable for me because it showed me clearly what gaps existed and what needed to be taught to her.

Along with this, we worked on specific concepts and the vocabulary needed to express them. Joan was learning to observe differences in movement and what terms to use to describe them like walking, jumping, running, flying, dancing, and hopping. She was also learning about differences in time; how to recognize them and what terms to use in connection with them like now and later, before and after, beginning and end, day and night, yesterday, today and tomorrow. She was learning about differences in content such as full and empty, and differences in size such as big and little, tall and short, narrow and wide, fat and thin, and so on. Most of this eluded her at first, but with persistent effort over a period of months, many of these concepts began to have some meaning.

Lotto games still served us well. The elementary ones such as the *Farm Lotto,* the *ABC Lotto,* and the *Look and Learn Lotto* had been excellent matching exercises. Since she was very adept at this by now, we merely used them for play. In addition, there were several more advanced ones that helped Joan to make connections that she still could not perceive herself. The *Go Together Lotto* was particularly good for this purpose. Joan learned about things belonging together like a mailbox and a letter, a fireman and a fire truck, a squirrel and a tree, a bathtub and soap, a bird and a cage. However, even when she could make the correct associations, she could not independently link the post office mailbox, the corner mailbox, or our house mailbox with the picture on the lotto card. Joan had to take another major step in her development before she could bridge this gap. It was not easily accomplished. This kind of training went on for months.

The lotto game, *The World Around Us,* taught Joan about pets, school, the weather, family, community workers, and so on. It introduced new vocabulary and many new concepts. She learned about the composition of a family, the services we receive from the postman, the milkman, and the policeman, the differences between animals and human beings, the concept of changing weather and changing seasons. Most of these ideas also were barely comprehensible at first. Here, too, we had to spend many months on them before she could really grasp them.

The *What's Missing Lotto* was excellent for developing Joan's perception. Before she was able to perceive what was missing on a cash register (the buttons), a chair (one leg), a ladder (the steps), a plane (the propeller), she had to have a picture in her mind of the whole unit. Since Joan had distorted views of most things, it was helpful to have her look through magazines and picture books so that she could see objects accurately portrayed and in their entirety. We talked about the unit and its components. In this way, Joan began to learn how to recognize the whole as well as the parts, and what the relationship was between them.

Joan's muddled view of the world was clearly evident in her drawings which continued to show marked disorientation. In the pictures she drew, a boy might have no ears, a four legged animal could have as many as seven or eight legs, an arm would sometimes be missing or be grossly misplaced. My husband and I observed that even when Joan's perception advanced to the point where her drawings became recognizable and more mature, she still almost always omitted ears from her drawings of boys and girls.

We were proceeding well with the sense training program. Joan understood the concept of variation in color, size, and quantity. Not only could she identify colors rather easily, but she could also arrange crayons of one color in varying shades ranging from light to dark. In the same way, she could readily differentiate between glasses containing varying amounts of liquid, and could place them in correct quantitative sequence. It was simple for her now to arrange buttons in the correct order according to size. She could also now arrange a pile of books of varying thicknesses in the right order. If I gave her mounds of caramels, each containing a different number of pieces, she could put them in proper sequence ranging from small groups to larger groups.

However, this was not sufficient because Joan still could not apply what she had learned to abstract situations. For instance, in crayoning a picture, she did not use color properly to distinguish between a shoe and a sock, the shirt and the trousers, and so on. She did not contain her colors within the outlines of the picture. This was probably due to the fact that she was generally unaware of what the pictures were trying to portray

In her choice of colors, Joan exhibited her lack of awareness of her environment. She colored bananas purple, grass black, apples blue, and then colored them in different unrealistic colors another time. Each shoe of a pair was usually colored differently. Yet, I never saw Joan put on a mismatched pair of shoes. Also, I am sure that if I had offered her a purple banana to eat, she would have rejected it. However, she had to be taught to observe that the mates of a pair of shoes are always colored the same. She also had to learn to ''see'' that bananas are yellow, and that in coloring them in a picture, we use a yellow crayon. Gradually, as her perception advanced, I could see improvement in this.

Joan's understanding of language was moving at a very slow pace. She had practically no ability to create images from words. All material had to be presented to her in the most visual terms possible. For this purpose, a group of simple books served us well.

One of them was a riddle book called *Guess Who Lives Here*. It was particularly good because the vocabulary was simple, the pictures were good, and the situations were familiar. We could act it out and identify all the characters and objects described in it. Joan enjoyed this book and learned from it something more about the world in which she was living. This book, used in conjunction with the lotto games and *The Golden Dictionary,* explained further the concepts of the family, pets, people who serve us, and changes in the day.

Another one that Joan loved was the riddle book entitled *What Am I.* It proved to be a good aid in teaching Joan how to listen for clues and how to interpret them. The riddles required Joan to recall and re-create learned facts.

The book *How Big* assisted Joan in understanding herself a little better in relation to the rest of the world. This was important because she was so confused in this particular area. She understood the concept of variable size such as big and little, and tall and short, but she struggled with the comparisons that were presented to establish the concept of relative size. We worked very hard on this with minimal success at this point.

In an attempt to stimulate Joan's imagination, I used the book *Come Play House,* but she had a great deal of difficulty with it. She enjoyed listening to the rhymes and loved the illustrations, but she did not understand the words. After working with it for several weeks, Joan was finally able to make some associations. When she learned to understand more words and ideas, the book became more meaningful.

Even though Joan did not comprehend most books yet, I read to her a great deal hoping the stories would stimulate her imagination and contribute something to her understanding of herself and the world. I used a large variety of books. Some were very simple Golden Books like *Baby's House, I Can Fly,* and *Daddies.* Others had more complicated story lines like *Frosty the Snowman, Fix it Please, The Happy Birthday Present, A Day at the Zoo,* and many others. Amongst the Wonder Books I read were *Peter Goes to School* which I used to prepare Joan for her own school experience, and a delightful animal story called *The Baby Elephant.* The Ding Dong series of books which included such stories as *I Decided, Debbie and Her Nap, My Big Brother,* and several others were excellent because they re-created real life situations that were familiar, to some extent, to Joan. She seemed to derive the most from these both in listening enjoyment and in learning because she could identify with the situations described. Another book that was a great favorite of Joan's was *The Very Little Girl,* a simple story of a small child growing up.

Before Joan could derive anything at all from any of these stories, I had to interpret them for her word for word. The ones that were easiest were those that described concrete, realistic situations. Stories that employed fantasy were meaningless and even irritating to her at this time. Imaginative stories like *The Pokey Little Puppy, The Blowaway Hat, Noises and Mr. Flibberty-Jib,* or *The Puppy Who Found a Boy* left Joan hopelessly bewildered. I had to postpone reading this kind of story for a while.

Along with the reading of books, I found it most helpful to continue inventing very simple stories that contained terms and concepts that Joan had already learned. She did not have to spar with these so energetically, and so could surrender herself more readily to the rhythm of the words and to some independent enjoyment of the story.

I continued to try to help Joan develop her imagination in every way I could. For instance, I would ask Joan to close her eyes while I said a single word like cup, book, or girl. I suggested that she try to see in her mind the picture my word evoked. Then I would ask her to describe the cup or book—the color, the size, the shape—anything at all she saw. When we first started, she would merely shrug her shoulders and say she saw nothing. It was difficult to determine whether that was because she did not understand my request or because she could not see an image. I am inclined to believe it was the latter. After several weeks of practice during which I demonstrated what I was asking her to do, she was able to do it successfully. We then went on to "see" and describe phrases and sentences dealing first with concretes like "eating an apple," "climbing a tree," "Alice writes with a pencil," and then with abstractions like "listen to me," or "I love animals." This was extremely difficult for her to do. As usual, Joan had much more success with concrete words than with abstract ones. In describing an image, if Joan's limited vocabulary prevented her from expressing herself, she had by now advanced to the level where she could use pantomine to show me, for instance, that a glass of milk had spilled, a policeman had stopped traffic, or a balloon had popped.

To make Joan more aware of the function of language, and to teach her how to listen and respond, I gave her simple directions to follow. I would ask her to "put the doll on the chair," "close the door," "give me a pencil," "bring me the glass," "roll the ball to me," and so on, giving her only one direction at a time. We did this for a brief period each day. At first, I had to repeat the direction several times. Finally, when she was better able to focus on what I was saying, she reacted more quickly. However, her responses were usually inaccurate because she seized upon the word or two that she understood and lost the rest. She could not grasp more than two or three words at a time. Also, she seemed to hear and comprehend only verbs and nouns. She had great difficulty with pronouns. In her own speech, Joan used only verbs, nouns, and proper nouns. Therefore, the direction "give me a pencil" was executed only if I was the only one in the room. Otherwise, she might give it to anyone. Terms such as who, what, where, how, when, and which made no sense to Joan whatsoever, so that, if I said, "Who has the book?" she might look at the book, but could not answer me. Parts of speech like prepositions, conjunctions, adjectives, adverbs, and articles were foreign to her.

Finally, after many, many weeks, when Joan was able to handle simple directions, I gave her more complex ones like "take the book from the table and put it on the chair." This was very difficult for her to execute because she could not retain both parts of the direction. I had to repeat it slowly three or four times, one part at a time, before she could respond to it. This kind of training eventually accomplished its purpose because it enabled her, when we began to use workbooks, to respond competently to directions in them. When so directed, she could put a sail on a boat, draw a ribbon on the girl's hair, or give the policeman a whistle.

Its most important consequence was to begin to teach Joan how to listen which was still a formidable task for her. She was learning words and ideas, but was using language lamely. There was some progress but it was slow. It was clear that Joan was still unable to understand, learn, and use words and to integrate experiences without going through a lengthy process each time.

Chapter 10

THE SUMMER BEFORE KINDERGARTEN

IN JUNE, WHEN JOAN was four years and eight months old, we enrolled her in a summer play school for a six week half day program. She loved to play outdoors, and the school provided a handsomely equipped play yard with a wading pool. For indoor play, there were the usual accoutrements in addition to craft and music activities. The groups were small and well supervised. The atmosphere was relaxed.

Joan accompanied me eagerly to play school each morning, but insisted that I stay with her. Despite all the efforts I made to reduce her dependence upon me, she still would not remain without me. I had to stay for the entire summer session.

Her activities again were largely unilateral, just as they had been in nursery school. However, she seemed happy to be playing alongside the children and occasionally made some effort to communicate with them. The children accepted her because she was very friendly and pleasant. However, the relationship could not be anything but limited because communication between them was so difficult. Her sentences, which contained only two or possibly three words, were poorly enunciated and indistinct. The children could not understand her. When they in turn spoke to her, she could only grasp a mere handful of words. Usually she lost the beginning of a sentence before it was finished. Very soon, most of them gave up trying to talk to her. If Joan felt rejected or abandoned, she gave no overt signs of this. Throughout the period, she tried from time to time to talk to the children. When bogged down again, she just continued going about her activities independent of them. I felt sad at seeing her thwarted in her own efforts to communicate, and at finding her uncomprehending of those playmates who persisted in trying to talk to her.

Joan and I had a larger measure of success in communicating with each other, but that was only because I knew how to reach her. When I spoke to her, I faced her towards me, raised my voice, made my statement brief and concise, used words she had learned already, enunciated clearly, and repeated my phrase several times. If I did not follow this procedure, she withdrew completely. I realized that no one else could possibly know how to approach her. Even if a person understood the problem, he could not be expected to make such an effort. Casual observers thought that Joan was merely inattentive, but we who understood Joan knew what an effort it was for her to listen and to speak. We always gave her every advantage.

However, the total picture was far from gloomy. Joan participated energetically in the physical aspects of the school. Here she had some small measure of contact with the children. She tumbled and splashed happily with them in the pool, climbed competitively on the monkey bars, raced them down the slides, and took her turn on the swings.

In arts and crafts, Joan performed minimally. She had to imitate the other children in order to participate even to the limited extent that she did. She explored the media with which the other children experimented, but stayed only briefly with each project. In the course of several weeks, her span of attention lengthened somewhat, and she began to understand the materials and goals better. Her use of them then improved a little.

When called upon to participate in group activities like marching, physical exercises, playing with musical instruments, and so on, she complied. Her comprehension here was better and she learned from these experiences.

Throughout the session, Joan received no indulgence from the staff. The teachers, for the most part, let her derive what she could from the experience without involving themselves with her in any special way. No pressures were brought to bear upon her as long as she remained a disciplined member of the group. She was now a most conforming child in the group situation. She sought and enjoyed approval from her contemporaries and her teachers just as she did at home. She had motivation within herself to become an accepted member of the group, and she had some understanding of how to achieve this. She was also comfortable with the structured experience. A well established routine, here as well as at home, was indeed reassuring to her. The fact that Joan could understand and use routine at this time represented considerable growth.

The play school experience, on the whole, was a positive one.

It helped bridge the gap between nursery school and kindergarten. It reinforced whatever Joan had learned at nursery school about group participation. It contributed to her social growth by providing her with companions and relationships that she was learning to understand a bit better. It gave Joan the opportunity to learn from her peers. Although the extent to which she could do this was difficult to assess, she did seem to be becoming a little more aware of the other children and the nature of their activities.

All this was most encouraging, but of far greater significance was the fact that Joan was seemingly happy at least a part of the day. This was reflected in her anticipation about going to play school in the morning, in her reluctance to leave at noontime, and the smiles on her face when she was enjoying some activity.

On Sundays, we often went on outings. We had picnics at the beach and Joan was usually very happy there. She was relaxed on the sand and in the water, and she enjoyed playing with her brothers. We went on fun rides at the amusement park and she enjoyed all the motion and activity. It was on a simple level and it was physical. Joan could understand this kind of experience.

We visited an animal farm set in a forest. Joan fed the animals in the cages, but was frightened when those that roamed freely came up to her. However, she enjoyed watching them romp and play.

We went to the zoo two or three times, and visited museums set in some of the parks. Joan became restless and impatient after a short time there. Initially, her interest in most of our activities was very brief, but as her comprehension grew, her staying power gradually increased. Each time an experience was repeated, she understood it a little better because there was beginning to be some recall.

Since eating in a restaurant was so exciting for the boys, we began to eat out occasionally, and Joan's behavior was very acceptable. She loved food and apparently found little in the experience of being in a strange place that could upset her unduly. Except for an occasional tantrum, eating out was a reasonably pleasant event, and we did it more often as time went on.

Generally, though, long trips amounting to more than one half hour, were difficult for Joan because she still disliked being confined in the car. She struggled and nagged throughout the ride. However, we continued to go out in the mornings every weekend, but tried to confine our activities to nearby places. When my husband was home on vacation, we also went out during weekdays.

At times, we questioned the validity of our outings in terms of Joan's reactions to the car rides, and in terms of the possible benefits she could derive from the actual experience. We concluded that these excursions were valid because the places we visited apparently did provide Joan with both pleasure and valuable opportunities to learn. They seemed to make her more alert and more aware of the world about her. As for the resistance she expressed in the car, although extremely annoying to all of us, it was bearable because it was relatively short lived. Joan calmed down as soon as we reached our destination. The over-all positives in this situation outweighed the negatives.

Our sons, of course, always enjoyed the trips tremendously. They were now seven, and nine and one half years old, respectively, and they were enthusiastic about almost everything. Although Joan consumed a major part of our time and thoughts, we always tried to provide our boys with what they needed too. We realized that most of the decisions we had made until now about vacations and outings had been based primarily on what we had felt was desirable for Joan. We had had little choice in this. In the past, we had been able to achieve some balance by having my husband take the boys out, without Joan and me, to see the sights in the city. He took them to the movies, to carnivals and fairs, on boat trips, to visit famous sites, and so on. Now that the time seemed opportune for including Joan in more of the activities, it was wonderful to be able to go out together more often as a family.

Throughout the entire summer period, the afternoon hours after naptime were devoted to the teaching program. This phase of Joan's life continued without interruption.

Chapter 11

JOAN IN KINDERGARTEN

Vacation time was now over. A program was planned for the coming year that would give Joan every opportunity to grow. She was scheduled to begin kindergarten, and work at the speech clinic, after a summer's recess, was to be resumed.

There was reason to feel hopeful about the future. In the year just passed, dramatic progress had indeed taken place. The changes had been significant ones both intellectually and emotionally. During this time, Joan had learned something about how to use and control her emotions. She had shown a capacity as well as a need for love. She had emerged a little from her totally introverted existence to form some relationships with the people around her. She now understood something about authority, discipline, and approval. She had begun to understand a little about what her needs were and how they are expressed and fulfilled. This, in turn, had enabled her to understand something about the needs and feelings of other people. The result had been greater sharing, less aggression, and more amenable behavior. It was her understanding, minimal as it was, of herself as a person that made it possible for her to use more advantageously the training she was getting.

Compared to the first three and one half to four years of Joan's life, the improvement we noted was indeed impressive. However, it was also apparent that she was still very far from being a well functioning child. Joan was still excessively self centered, demanding, and immature. She whined and tugged at me a great deal. The difference between before and now was essentially one of degree. I can only guess that this behavior was probably due to the fact that she still could not sufficiently understand and express herself in words, and still could not adequately comprehend the order of her existence. She experienced a great deal of frustration.

Considering Joan's general disorientation, I found it surprising that she submitted herself so willingly to the difficult learning disciplines I imposed upon her. She came quickly when I called her and sat compliantly and seemingly happy at our work table. For several hours each day, she harnessed her will and her intellectual resources to a demanding process. Part of this was due to the fact that she always enjoyed having my absolute attention. However, some small part of it must have emanated from a subtle awareness of her own needs, and some indefinable understanding of my tremendous desire to help her. In any event, I recall these hours as being the only ones that were free of conflict.

There was a good amount of pressure on Joan to respond, and I was concerned lest this harm her emotionally. However, there was nothing I could observe in her behavior to indicate that this training program was having any adverse effect upon her. Joan seemed to have a self preserving mechanism within her that protected her. When challenged beyond her capabilities, she withdrew. This was the only overt sign of resistance she gave to warn me that I was making excessive demands upon her. We took time out for a rest at these points. I then recaptured her attention and released her finally when convinced that she had exhausted her resources for that day. When dismissed from the learning session, she bounced off her chair and went briskly on her way. She did not share my complete feeling of exhaustion. Although the amount of energy she expended with me seemed small, I believe that it truly represented the limit of her abilities. She seemed not able to give more than just a tiny part of herself.

On the intellectual level, her progress was substantial. Joan had learned something about the whys and wherefores of the world. She had learned some concepts and words, and was now communicating a little. However, she was still essentially inarticulate. More words and ideas had to be integrated before she could begin to use language properly. She was also still unable to comprehend words and experiences without my help. We had hoped that she would pick up momentum after the basic groundwork had been laid. However, there was still no evidence that she could learn in the usual way. Even with maximum help, her advance was still halting and laborious.

Although our emotional involvement with Joan sent my husband and me gyrating between alternating moods of elation and despair, certain facts emerged from these assessments. The approach was valid. With it, the prognosis for the future looked good. Without it, it was more than likely that further development might cease. This was more than just an assumption. Any relaxation of the training program seemed to result not only in arrested growth, but indeed, in regression. This led us to the steadfast conviction that all possible efforts had to be continuously directed towards helping Joan fulfill the potential she possessed. We believed more than ever that she was well endowed, and felt quite confident that ultimately we would see Joan emerge as an integrated person.

Before the kindergarten session began, Joan and I started working on special exercises that the speech pathologist recommended in our third contact. Joan had advanced to the level where she seemed capable of beginning to learn how to think. This was a process that was still strange to her. All observations led us to conclude that this ability, like so many others, would have to be developed in Joan. She had great difficulty concentrating, and her span of attention continued to be too brief for concentrated work. The following exercises were designed to help her focus her attention on a given problem and to think it through to its solution. They were also geared to teaching her how to respond better to directions. As with all experiences, we hoped that they would widen the scope of her understanding by providing her with specific information, new vocabulary, and new concepts which she still needed to learn. Some of these exercises offered the additional advantage of helping her to develop her well functioning small muscles to an even finer degree.

To begin with, I drew figures such as these:

FIGURE 1

and asked Joan to trace them several times with her finger. Then I asked her to reproduce them on paper. Incidentally, I observed that Joan was consistently right handed. Every day, I noted improvement in the way she used her pencil and in the way she perceived the different shapes. There was a change within two or three weeks from shaky poorly reproduced figures to firm disciplined strokes. This contrasted very markedly from the rate at which she acquired verbal skills. After a slow laborious teaching process, Joan learned the names of the figures. I could then draw the forms helter skelter in varying sizes on a page and ask her to point to a square, a circle, a rectangle, an A, a cross, and so on. When she could do this, I would then ask her to find a *big* cross, a *small* circle, a *small* square, a *big* triangle, and so on. As I introduced new forms such as:

LCUT⌐⊥

FIGURE 2

she automatically traced them with her finger and then drew them. She enjoyed the activity and participated eagerly. Her comprehension of what we were trying to achieve was good.

As soon as Joan was ready to deal with more complex directions, I introduced the words inside and around. I would present the following forms to her:

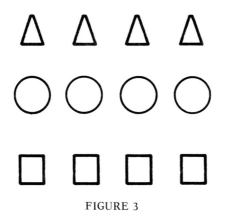

FIGURE 3

and direct her to put a square *inside* the triangle, a cross *inside* the circle, and a circle *inside* the square. From these, we went on to exercises that required her to put a square *around* the circle, a circle *around* the triangle, and so forth. After much practice with these, she was ready to handle different directions such as putting a cross *inside* the triangle, a circle *around* the circle, a triangle *inside* the square, and so on. Next came the process of teaching Joan the terms *first* and *last,* the cardinal numbers *one, two, three,* and so on, and the ordinals *first, second, third,* etc. After a good deal of hard work, Joan could, in response to verbal directions, put a square inside the *first* triangle, a number *one* inside the *second* triangle, and a circle inside the *last* triangle thus:

FIGURE 4

I used these words in connection with practical situations, and so required her to apply what she had learned to everyday experiences. When I asked her to put a spoon *inside* a drawer, a rubberband *around* a book, a scarf *around* her shoulders, a ribbon *around* her hair, or a picture *inside* a book, she was confused at first. It took additional time to teach her how to use these words when they were presented in different contexts.

I also introduced the words *up, down,* and *across* within new contexts and combined them with words she knew already. Thus, Joan learned to draw a line *across* a square like this:

FIGURE 5

two lines *across* a square like this:

FIGURE 6

or three lines *across* a triangle like this,

FIGURE 7

when directed to do so. She learned to connect two dots by drawing a line *down,* then *across* to another dot, and *up* to a fourth dot. She then finished the square. The exercise looked like this:

FIGURE 8

Specific words like *up* and *down* were still very difficult for Joan to understand and she struggled with them. After the vocabulary was learned, I tried to establish the concepts of form and position by using many variations of these exercises on the work sheets.

Joan did these exercises for a few minutes at a time several times each day for a few weeks. Reproducing the forms was relatively easy for her because she could handle motor experiences and concrete learning well. However, she had to work very hard and long to come to grips with the vocabulary and the concepts. With constant repetition, she finally did achieve a great deal. Joan enjoyed her success. She was definitely learning how to concentrate, how to think, and how to respond to language. Despite this progress, there was very little improvement in her ability to speak.

Joan could recognize her own name now when she saw it and wanted to learn how to write it. She accomplished this rather quickly, and was delighted with her achievement. She was actually responding quite magnificently to the learning situation now. We continued to note an acceleration in the rate at which she was able to acquire new skills.

While all this was going on, Joan was continuing at the speech clinic. In September, she had been assigned to a new speech therapist whom she rejected at first, but accepted shortly thereafter. This year, we who worked with Joan felt that we could be firmer in dealing with her. It seemed to us that her comprehension was developed enough to allow her to understand the process of being separated and reunited with me after a session. Contrary to this expectation, she clung possessively to me, and insisted that I go into the therapy room with her. I stayed a few minutes and then walked out. However, I had to remain within her view outside the door because she seemed genuinely frightened if she could not see me. Neither the speech therapist nor I could reassure her about the fact that I would not leave her and go away. It was extremely difficult to determine how much of her reaction was due to lack of understanding, real insecurity, or a desire to control. To guard against upsetting her unnecessarily, I weaned her away firmly but sensitively, and whenever possible, with her cooperation. After several weeks, I found that I could just walk out of the therapy room without having Joan "fall to pieces." I never, even for an instant, gave her any reason to lose confidence in me. She always found me where I told her I would be.

The goals at the clinic were essentially the same as they had been during the preceding year. The new therapist also hoped to develop Joan's speech and wanted to help her relate better to people and to her environment. Joan's speech was very halting, and the words she said were indistinct and monosyllabic. She still spoke in a monotone. No attention was given at the clinic to any speech correction because it was considered far more important to stimulate and encourage a flow of words. I was not so well disciplined, and found myself correcting her enunciation a great deal.

After most clinic sessions, the speech therapist, who was an accepting and loving person, spent a few minutes with me discussing Joan's progress and sharing materials and ideas. I benefited greatly from the suggestions she offered me, and tried to continue at home, whenever possible, the direction being followed at the clinic. The staff social worker continued to have regular conferences with me during this time. She contributed her objectivity and knowledge in an effort to assist me towards achieving a greater understanding of how best to handle Joan. These sympathetic contacts also gave me the opportunity to learn what the clinic was expecting to accomplish and to what extent they were succeeding.

All the people, the speech pathologist, the clinic staff, and the school personnel, involved in Joan's development, maintained a regular contact with one another in a determined effort to give Joan every possible advantage. My husband and I were never alone in our continuing efforts to help Joan, but the burden of implementing her growth seemed more and more to rest with the home program. What could be accomplished in the limited hours at the clinic, and what she could derive from a group school experience, was inadequate in terms of her needs. It seemed that only my constant efforts of both a formal and informal nature could yield significant results.

In September, Joan, not yet five years old, started school. We were delighted to see how fully competent she was in taking care of her physical needs. She handled her rubbers, boots, and clothes with its assorted bows, buttons and zippers with ease. Well aware of her achievements, she showed proud independence in this area of her living. This pride in her skills was further reflected in her now orderly care of her toys and room at home.

Joan joined an average kindergarten group of fourteen children supervised by a teacher and an assistant teacher. This was the same private school in our community where she had attended nursery school for a brief session the previous spring. We chose to have her attend here rather than public school because the classes were small and she would be with the same group of children with which she had been in nursery school.

Now that Joan was in a formal school situation, I thought it more appropriate that she wear dresses. Until this point, she had worn slacks most of the time because they were most comfortable for play. Suddenly, we became embroiled in a daily argument about her clothes. I tried to explain why I wanted her to wear a dress to school. This discussion brought into focus the fact that although Joan could distinguish between boys and girls in books, in school, and in the playground, she was very confused about what she was. Sometimes she would say she was a girl, and sometimes she would say she was a boy. In school she would usually line up with the boys to go outside, would seek out the boys' activities and toys, and would stay with the boys most of the time. Of course, much of this was due to the fact that she was growing up with two brothers, but no small part of it was due to her lack of understanding of herself. At home, she still did not differentiate too clearly between her father and me because she did not yet understand our separate roles well enough. Joan had every opportunity to observe our different functions. For instance, she saw me cook, clean, and sew, and observed her father fixing broken toys, mowing the lawn, and going to work each day. Yet her lack of clarity persisted.

In kindergarten, Joan was accepted and liked by her group. The children remembered each other from their previous association. Again, Joan did not receive any special privileges from the teacher. It was expected only that she participate in all the activities to the best of her ability. Joan was frightened and confused at first because of her lack of understanding of her new environment. Here was a new room, a new teacher, and new routines to which she had to become accustomed.

Again, she insisted that I stay with her in the room.

As the weeks went by, Joan relaxed a little just as she was relaxing at the speech clinic, and she began to perceive, to a small extent, a pattern in her life. She was pleased about going to school and seemed to understand the procedure of getting ready to go there each morning. In school, her awareness of a routine came first in connection with cookie time. She was able to anticipate this event and enjoyed it tremendously. As her understanding of her environment increased, she became more secure and could begin to let go of me. By December fifteenth, I was able to bring Joan to school and leave her for the half day session. She continued the school year alone and experienced no setbacks.

During the months that I remained in the kindergarten room, I had an excellent opportunity to observe Joan with her contemporaries. I noted the tremendous language gaps that still existed between her and her classmates, and this stimulated me to make even greater efforts with Joan. I also observed the teaching techniques in the classroom, and I found I could use them constructively at home.

In this school, the teaching of number concepts preceded the reading program. The Catherine Stern block method of arithmetic was taught. I learned how to use the material and bought a unit, so that I could keep Joan at her proper school level. This method employed the concrete approach to number learning and was ideally suited to Joan's needs. She took her place in her small learning group and involved herself as fully as she could in the learning experience. However, she was immediately at a disadvantage because she did not know the vocabulary necessary for learning the number concepts.

In this arithmetic system, the pupil learns the relationships between numbers by understanding the relationship between blocks of proportionate length. For example, the one-block is a one-inch cube of a specific color. The two-block is equal to two one-blocks, the three-block is equal to three one-blocks, and so on. The color designation, which is different in every block from one to ten, is used consistently throughout the set. With amazing rapidity, the children learned the relationships between the blocks and the proper number names. A six-block that equaled six one-blocks in length was a concrete fact. The blocks from one to ten could be arranged into stairs. It was immediately obvious to the child when the stairs were incorrectly constructed or had missing steps. The use of numerals was postponed until the number concepts were well learned. However, Joan and most of the others recognized and used them early in the year.

The transition to the learning of addition was relatively easy. If a five-block equaled five one-blocks, the child soon found out that other combinations also equalled a five-block. For example, a two-block and a three-block, a three-block and a two-block, a one-block and a four-block, and a four-block and a one-block all equalled a five-block. The children worked with all the combinations up to a ten-block. They could actually "see" the numbers. This was not rote learning. There were many exercises designed to increase their understanding of the number concepts and improve their facility with numbers. The writing of arithmetic sums and differences came at the end of the year. It was handled with relative ease by most of the children including Joan.

While Joan could deal with this concrete system very nicely, she was confused by the new words and by the old words in new contexts. When the group was directed to mix up the blocks and put them in correct order according to size, Joan did not understand the direction at all. She would merely observe the other children, pick up her cues, and then proceed with her task. When she had to function independently, she did not know what was expected of her and failed. She tried very, very hard, but the language was simply beyond her comprehension. We spent many hours at home learning this new vocabulary. I had to interpret idiomatic expressions for her because she kept trying to interpret them literally. Joan was completely confused by such phrases as *mix up, place in order, build some stairs, hold up a three-block, hand me, show me, place behind your back,* and so on. It took constant language work throughout the year to keep her functioning within the group. When she finally grasped the vocabulary, she dealt well with the number concepts.

About midpoint in the kindergarten year, Joan mastered the alphabet very rapidly. Her learning here proceeded at what would be considered a normal rate, and she became very adept at identifying the letters in her alphabet book. She learned the alphabet song in school and retained it well. Her memory was certainly improving. It was wonderful to see her make such progress.

I became extremely vigilant about having Joan avoid rote learning.

Until this point, this had not posed any problem because her memory had been so very poor that she had scarcely been able to recall anything from one minute to the next. Now that she was demonstrating that she could retain material like the alphabet by memorizing it, I had to be very watchful lest she learn merely by rote. For example, Joan was beginning to recite nursery rhymes, but she could not understand their meanings. She could now name vegetables and fruits pictured in her books by rote, but could not name them as I took them out of the refrigerator at random. I checked her comprehension of words and ideas constantly.

During all these months our work at home continued to advance. In addition to all the books and materials I had been using, I constantly found others that seemed to meet Joan's specific needs. Some that I used and liked were *Playbook for Small Fry, Playtime and Storytime,* and *It's Fun to Learn.* Much of this was reading readiness material and served well to sharpen Joan's perception. In addition, they alerted me to concepts and words that Joan had not learned as yet and needed to know. Joan enjoyed using these books. Other examples of books we used that provided additional exercises in number and reading readiness were *Stories to Read—Pictures to Color—Games to Play, Count-Color-Play, Beginning Arithmetic, Fun with Writing, Quizzle Book of Things that Move, Happy Times with Numbers,* and a picture book entitled *I Learn My Numbers.* I also used a set of flash cards called *Picture Words for Beginners,* and the *Play Way Alphabet Flash Cards.*

As soon as Joan learned the symbols for numbers, at about the age of five, she enjoyed working with simple dot books. Each dot was labeled with a number. By connecting the dots in numerical order, she formed an image which she could identify and color. Following the dots gave her facility with the number symbols. As her perception improved, she began to recognize any number errors she made by noting that a picture resulted that she could not identify. This was particularly good training for her, and also provided her with hours of very enjoyable activity.

Joan was still exhibiting great unawareness of her own body in her figure drawings. To help her with this, the speech therapist at the clinic suggested that Joan trace figures of people in magazines and then cut them out. Joan's lack of integration was dramatically demonstrated here. She usually cut off heads and snipped off parts of the body. When I saw this, I decided to give her pictures of simple objects such as a carrot, a whistle, or a ball to outline with her finger and then cut out. When she could do this accurately, we advanced to pictures of animals and people. It actually took several months of training before she could do this at all perceptively. This practice helped Joan to understand herself and her environment a little better.

Through the years, Joan always achieved a better understanding of her environment by actually experiencing the things we were talking about. Since she was still very confused about different kinds of stores, I took her on many trips to them so she could learn about shopping and money. She also learned specifically where I went when I wanted to buy toys, drugs, clothes, food, and so on. After several months, she acquired some degree of clarity about the services of different stores and could begin to tell me where I could buy toothpaste, bread, books, dresses, and so on. We used toy models of stores, and tried to re-create our experiences over and over again. It was exceedingly difficult for Joan to learn about the use of money, how to identify coins, and what the difference was between buying and selling. Two books, *Five Pennies to Spend* and *Let's Go Shopping* were somewhat helpful in this area of learning. However, the use of money eluded Joan during this entire year.

A particularly good aid in teaching Joan discrimination and the function of everyday objects was to give her a few minutes of the following game each day. She had already learned the names of various common tools, so I would ask her to tell me what she would use when she sewed (needle, thimble, scissors, thread, fabric), when she played (ball, doll, blocks, crayons, carriage), when she ate (spoon, fork, plate), cut out pictures (scissors), went fishing (pole, hooks, net, bait), hung up wet clothes (clothes pins, line), baked cakes (pans, measuring cup, spoon, flour, eggs, milk), fixed a toy (hammer, screw driver, screws, nails), and so forth. At first, Joan could only point to the object in her picture books, or actually find it and bring it to me. When Joan brought me the tool or showed me the picture, she was usually correct because she understood what I was asking for. However, when I asked her merely to tell me the names of these objects, she became very confused and called a pan a doll, and when she meant to say thread, she might say spoon. This pointed up so clearly how much more language training Joan needed.

Teaching Joan that we use different clothes for different activities and for different weather conditions was very difficult because this was such an abstract idea. When she finally grasped it, and I asked her how to dress for sleep, for snow play, or for the beach, she could bring me the correct garment, but could not name it. Speech always trailed behind her laboriously gained comprehension.

Joan's general ability to listen, to comprehend words, and to respond to them was still proceeding slowly. The following method that I used required her to listen closely and to make a decision. I would say to her, "What should I do with this candy?" She would usually look at me with a confused or even blank expression on her face indicating that little had registered. I would then give her two choices. "Should I wash it?" or "Should I eat it?" Usually, Joan could not answer me, so I would help her "see" the two possibilities by using gestures. Only when I helped her in this way, did she see the incongruity of one of the choices. She would then give me the correct answer. In most concrete situations, where no language was required, Joan responded intelligently. For instance, she knew where household things belonged, could put groceries away efficiently, and so on, but she was trapped when she had to respond verbally to any of these situations.

During the next months, I was able to teach her how to interpret words and imagine the action without my help. When she was finally able to make the correct choice between two possibilities, I gave her three or four options. From there I went on to incorporate two logical choices, with one representing the better answer. This required a finer degree of judgment. Over a period of a year, I saw definite improvement in Joan's concentration and ability to think.

Towards the end of the kindergarten year, Joan began to ask me about words on signs, cereal boxes, books, and so on. Since she knew her alphabet very well, she was simply curious about what various combinations of letters signified. One day, I opened a Scott Foresman pre-primer and sounded out two or three words for her. To my great astonishment, she remembered them the next day, and could reproduce them wherever and whenever she saw them. I increased the number of words each day and she retained them well. She was using a combination of phonics and sight-reading to recall them. Joan enjoyed her success tremendously and preferred this learning activity to any other.

However, this turned out to be a purely mechanical process. She had absolutely no comprehension of the meanings of the words or phrases she read. She was able to go through an entire pre-primer fluently without comprehending one single idea. Even the picture clues did not help her because she was not able to associate the words with the pictures as yet. Her ability to read was far advanced over her language comprehension. From the very beginning of her reading experience, Joan always read from left to right, never inverted words, and always read from the top to the bottom of the page.

At this time, Joan's speech was difficult to understand because it was poorly articulated. Vowel sounds were distorted. She tended to omit S sounds and final consonants. However, by looking at the printed word, she could sound it out much more accurately than when she merely heard it. This is how she began to overcome some of the difficulties she experienced because of her poor language reception. For example, she had always said bu for book, bre for bread, ru for run, and so forth. Now that she could read the words, she enunciated the final consonants. However, her difficulty with S sounds persisted, and she continued to say kool for school, ope for soap, li-en for listen, and so on. Joan's improvement in articulation was slow, but she was definitely making progress.

An evaluation of the school year which was now well advanced, yielded a positive picture. Joan had accepted the necessary disciplines, and had exhibited the normal behavior of a lively child. She had formed some relationships, and had enjoyed being with her peers. She had achieved academically, but most of her learning had occurred at home because of the intensive individual teaching program we had. However, we could not have accomplished as much as we did without the school because I needed the guideposts and techniques that the school was providing. Of all the advantages that the school offered, the most important was the social experience that Joan was getting.

For the first time in her life, Joan had a favorite friend. This was a little boy in school whom she wanted to be with constantly. She spoke of him, and tried to share her feelings about him with me. Most of the other children seemed to like her too, and accepted her as one of the group. They showed little overt concern with her difficulty in expressing herself. She seemed unaware of how limited her own participation was in their conversation and imaginative play. She and the other youngsters seemed to accept each other's individual differences.

I had regular conferences with Joan's teacher who told me that her progress was satisfactory and that she exhibited growth. Most of the school day was free of problem, but Joan was restless when confronted with language activities. During story time, for example, she withdrew and still seemed to derive nothing from the experience. Although she resented being confined, she respected the rules and remained quietly with the group.

Fortunately, much of the material used at the kindergarten level was non-verbal. Joan enjoyed the playground, the games, the paints, crayons, blocks, and so on, even though her comprehension of the facilities at her disposal was limited. Her span of attention was still very brief. She flitted from one thing to another and excitedly tried everything. As soon as she began to understand the nature of her activities better, her span of attention lengthened, and there was improvement in her use of the school materials.

In the playground at school and at home, Joan still walked and ran with her arms raised and bent at the elbows, but there was improvement. I do not know what connection there was between Joan's language impairment and the way she walked, but it seemed to us that as she learned more language, there was a corresponding improvement in her large muscle coordination.

The teacher shared Joan's portfolio of art work with me, and her experiments with finger paints were very revealing. She tried the medium reluctantly at first, and produced only large non-definitive masses in dark colors such as black, gray, brown, and purple. The paintings were obviously immature. The teacher reported that Joan exhibited impatience by tearing her work into shreds if she did not remove it from Joan's table immediately after Joan had stopped painting. Generally, within the group, the children showed their growth in their finger paintings. With the passing of time, their early non-definitive impressions turned into recognizable forms. By the end of the year, their pictures had story content. Joan developed too, but her growth was much slower. In time, she began to use color more freely. Her forms became more controlled and she began to put color where she wanted it. At the end of the year, we could see the suggestion of a house, a tree, or a man, and she was using mainly bright colors like reds and yellows. Joan was beginning to see, react, recall, and reproduce.

She responded exceptionally well to the reading readiness program in the second half of the year. The training she had been receiving at home prepared her well for this experience. When she took her achievement tests in May, she scored remarkably well. Her place in this average kindergarten group was at the top of the lower half. The school psychologist with whom I had two or three contacts in the latter half of this school year recommended to the school administration that Joan be advanced to the first grade in the fall. She had observed Joan in the classroom and had analyzed her test records. She was confident that Joan could handle the first grade curriculum if I worked intensively with her during the summer. Her suggestion was that Joan receive from me the assistance she needed in the language areas where she lagged seriously behind her contemporaries. She testified to Joan's good learning potential and gave me material that would help me to develop it.

Our fourth interview with the speech pathologist took place in April. She was very pleased when she observed the progress that Joan was making, and reinforced the program with further teaching suggestions. She also noted that Joan's behavior was still extremely immature. We all felt that growth in this area would proceed as soon as Joan acquired more language.

The school year ended and we made plans for a busy summer. Although Joan had made substantial progress during this past year, she was still very difficult to live with. She nagged a great deal and made excessive demands. Joan still did not comprehend and hence could not accept the fact that she was only one part of a family group. She expected an abundance of attention from me. This differed markedly from her attitude in school where she had seemed to accept the fact that she was only one amongst several others who had to share the attention of the teacher. This fortunate circumstance was probably what had enabled her to remain in school. Is it possible that she knew somehow how tenuous her school relationships with the teacher and the pupils were as compared to her relationships in a loving home with parents who accepted her regardless of her behavior?

JOAN AT THE AGE OF FIVE YEARS AND NINE MONTHS

Chapter 12

THE SUMMER WHEN JOAN WAS FIVE AND ONE-HALF

Joan RETURNED TO THE summer play school that she had attended the previous year. It was a six week, half day session again. From the very first day, she was able to go there and stay without me. It was a happy summer, but Joan's activities were again essentially unilateral. She enjoyed physical activity, handled herself well during structured periods like painting, swimming, games, and so on, but she scarcely ever communicated with the children. She tried to, of course, but they still did not understand her. Joan did not enjoy being alone, and usually joined a group. The children seemed to like her and often tried to include her in their activities. She seemed to be having fun and looked forward to seeing the children each day. When the morning was over, we returned home, and after Joan had had her nap, we started our afternoon work schedule.

After the play school experience was over, we left as a family for a five week stay in an Adirondack Mountain cabin. Joan adjusted remarkably well to the change. We worked each morning for two to three hours, and after lunch and a nap, she enjoyed an afternoon of free play.

This was Joan's first experience away from familiar surroundings and there were no problems except for her fear of the electrical storms which came on suddenly and fiercely in the mountains. Joan had always feared lightening and thunder. The summer storms were so violent and frequent that her fear of them increased. She woke up in the night when they occurred, but she could be reassured. We could use words to explain what was happening, and she could understand our attempts to console her. She would calm down after a little while. How different this was from the little girl who, such a very short time before, had been so unreachable.

Joan loved fishing. Her brothers had taught her how to fish and now competed with her. She hung patiently from a boat or over a dock waiting for a nibble. She caught many fish and handled her line, bait, and catch very competently. Joan joined her brothers in their ball games, and she tried to be a good team mate. I believe that this was the first time the boys considered her an equal rather than just a baby. She had to learn to respect the rules of the game because they expected good sportsmanship from her. Since she loved playing with them, she tried very hard to be "one of the boys." Sometimes it worked. Often it did not. In this, she was not too different from her contemporaries.

Joan also spent hours on the beach with her friends playing happily in the water and on the sand. She copied the play castles, forts, and tunnels the others created for their imaginative stories, and cheerfully made whatever contributions she could.

We went on picnics, visited new beaches, climbed a tall mountain, and made trips to an Adirondack museum, an historical fort, an animal farm, and a fairy tale re-creation. Again Joan was impatient when confined to the car too long. However, these trips were meaningful to her because she could now bring to them what she remembered of past experiences. We could discuss them to some small extent. She also always enjoyed roaming amongst colorful, fanciful exhibits.

Besides having a good deal of fun and freedom, this was also a summer of concentrated work for Joan. Equipped with the Dolch reading readiness material, ten pre-primers, and workbooks of all kinds that I either borrowed from the school psychologist or bought, Joan and I faced even more vigorous work sessions than we had had until this point. Her understanding of the number concepts was approximately at the proper level, so we devoted just a small portion of the work period to a review of them. Most of the time was occupied with language study. I continued using the same word study books, lottos, puzzles, and games that I had used before, but now I was working with them on a still more advanced level. We read all the pre-primers during the summer months and completed many work book exercises designed to further her comprehension.

As Joan's base line of vocabulary grew broader, and her conceptual knowledge increased, I expected her to acquire greater facility in handling new words and concepts. This did not happen. The same teaching process we were continually involved in had to be pursued with every new word because Joan still did not exhibit any evidence that she could learn by herself. Even if I demonstrated a word, or incorporated it in a sentence, she was still unable to decipher its meaning independently. The all important difference now, was that she was able to learn words a little faster and retain them a bit more easily.

We noted a decided improvement in Joan's speech. This was due in part to rhythmical reading exercises in her pre-primers such as, "Jump up, Rags, Jump up; Come Rags, Jump up." Joan was getting from this the idea of phrases and sentences.

In addition, I was now using a specific technique that the speech pathologist had suggested to me in our April contact to help Joan improve her auditory memory. This method required Joan to repeat after me a series of nonsense syllables. We started with two or three of them at first. Then gradually we increased the number to four or five, but added only one syllable at a time. Joan was required to listen to me say them once, and then to repeat them after me. The syllables were without any meaning (*ka-to, pay-le-to, ti-so-ray-ko, po-la-si-kay-me,* and so on), and I selected them at random. Joan did well with these exercises. They proved to be good aids in helping her to understand the process of listening better. They also improved her articulation a little and helped sharpen her ability to recall. We found that she could repeat words just as she repeated nonsense syllables, but unfortunately, she did not understand their meanings unless they were fully explained to her.

As a result of all these efforts, Joan was gradually able to say three or four words consecutively without losing her thought. However, it was still wholly restricted to nouns and verbs. She would say, "eat green bean," "Joan play ball," "Daddy sing Joan song," and so on. Slowly, her monosyllabic speech developed into polysyllabic speech. We were delighted with her constant progress. Speech was indeed limited, but Joan was communicating at last.

Joan and I worked on rhymes like man, can, fan, pan, and ran, in order to teach her how to attack new words. She took note of the different initial consonants and learned very rapidly how to decipher the new word. These exercises sharpened Joan's auditory perception, increased her vocabulary, and improved her understanding of phonics. She responded quickly and intelligently to this and loved playing with rhyming syllables. I realized that she was finally hearing words when she began to question me about new ones she formed and did not recognize. For instance, in looking for words to rhyme with man, she zealously ran through the alphabet. This produced words that made no sense like lan or zan. When this happened, she would sometimes look at me quizzically and ask if those were words

Although Joan was now responding well to verbal directions on a concrete level such as, "put the books away on the shelf," "open your arithmetic book to page six," and so on, she was still at a loss as how to proceed when confronted with textbook directions employing abstract words. Given a new direction, she gave no sign of even having heard it. Automatically, she duplicated the process she had just completed whether it made sense or not. However, since the variety of directions in her books was limited, I was eventually able to train her to respond to them correctly. In time, when directed to do the following; *connect pictures and phrases, put a circle around, color, number in the correct order, cross out the one that does not match, complete the picture,* and so on, Joan could respond appropriately. She learned to recognize all of the standard types of exercises contained in her work books, and knew exactly what to do with them without getting specific directions from me. If, however, the instructions given with an exercise were altered, she was confused. Joan was still relying heavily on her excellent ability to "see" what was required of her, rather than on language.

At this stage of her development, Joan experienced her greatest language difficulties when dealing with idiomatic expressions. She had already acquired a fair base of abstract and concrete terms. However, she was completely literal, and when she encountered groups of words that meant something entirely different from what each word interpreted individually meant, she was totally bewildered. Normally, speech is so automatic, we do not realize how many idioms our language contains. I found out. I was newly stunned by the magnitude of the job before me. How could I possibly explain to this child who had trouble enough with abstract words, the meaning of such phrases as, "How do you feel?" "Can you tell time?", or "I cannot stand this weather." I shared with Joan the word for word translation of these phrases in an effort to help her distinguish between the literal and the functional meanings of idioms. Most of them were really ridiculous, and Joan and I decided that ours was indeed a very peculiar language. In terms of teaching idioms, there was nothing we could do except plod through mazes of words. We found no shortcuts to learning here.

As the summer drew to a close, my husband and I felt, for the first time since Joan was born, that we had experienced some joy in her company. However, her care remained burdensome because she was still struggling with the concept of time as it related to the meeting of her needs. Any delay in complying with her requests made her very impatient and resulted in nagging. I felt that she was responding in this way because she was not yet aware of the fact that I had other responsibilities and would attend to her needs in due course. As she acquired more language, she began to understand this a little better with the result that she started to become somewhat more accepting and a bit more relaxed. Unfortunately though, this proceeded very slowly.

Observing Joan day after day, we felt troubled about the future. Even though Joan had made almost unbelievable progress in the two years since we had first sought help for her, we wondered if she could ever learn enough language to become fully independent of my teaching. It was, as always, an all encompassing activity for both of us, involving almost every moment of the day. I still needed to teach her words. I was also still teaching her how to listen, how to think, how to reason, and how to form conclusions. I was training her how to observe, how to interpret what she saw, and how to recall and use learned facts. Of course, we were constantly reaching higher levels, but it was never an independent process. I felt encouraged only when I reminded myself that words and ideas that Joan had seemed incapable of understanding only a short time before, were now well within her grasp. When I was feeling most discouraged, I noted Joan's budding efforts to "tune in" on general conversation around her, and I knew that we had indeed come a long way.

September arrived and Joan was scheduled to enter first grade. We elected to have her continue at the same private school she had attended the previous year rather than have her transfer to a public school. We made this decision because the classes were very small, the teaching staff was competent, I was able to communicate easily with the staff, and the curriculum was advanced over the public school program. We were confident that Joan could get a good education there. Most important of all, Joan was comfortable and happy in this school setting and was making progress within it.

Chapter 13

JOAN ENTERS FIRST GRADE

JOAN, NOT QUITE SIX years old, entered first grade as one of the youngest pupils in her class. By a curious twist of fate, the accident of prematurity, which advanced her birthdate three months, put her in a class one year ahead of the one she would have been in had she been a full term baby.

Our home teaching program gave her a slight academic advantage over her classmates. Joan could read while most of the others could not as yet. However, they soon caught up to her, and then it was my responsibility to keep her as close to fulfilling the curriculum requirements as possible. I had excellent cooperation from her teacher who liked Joan and was warmly sympathetic to her problems. She suggested ways of handling certain learning impasses, gave me methods with which she had experimented, and pointed out areas of weakness that needed reinforcement. Joan's reading comprehension was lagging seriously, and she was beginning to reject reading. She liked the sounds of the words and enjoyed saying them, but was upset by the demands made upon her to understand what she was reading. At her teacher's suggestion, I dissected the material down to units that were small enough for Joan to handle. We worked first with phrases, then with whole sentences, and then with paragraphs. I never continued with a new unit unless I was sure that she had grasped the material we had already worked on. During the entire year, Joan could not handle units larger than a two or three sentence paragraph. It took her all of first grade before she could even begin to grasp the concept of who was speaking and to whom the action in a given sentence referred.

During our fifth contact with the speech pathologist in September of this year, she again was pleased with Joan's progress thus far, and gave us suggestions for helping her further. Since Joan was still not asking questions as a young child normally does, the speech pathologist suggested that I ask them for her. In this way, Joan could

98

begin to understand the process of asking questions and getting answers. For example, I might say, "Why do we water flowers?" If she could not answer me, I helped her. I would suggest several possible answers in an attempt to assist Joan in developing the thought. After a few weeks of this kind of practice, Joan began to ask questions herself. We knew then that she was beginning to think independently.

Joan always loved listening to nursery rhymes even though she was still making little progress in understanding them. She tried to interpret them literally and ended up more confused than ever. However, it occurred to me that I might be able to use their rhythmical quality to good advantage in trying to improve the quality of her voice. It was, at that time, very unpleasant to listen to because it was shrill and high pitched. There was very little variation in tone. When reciting, I exaggerated my speech inflections, and read the poems in a sing song voice. All that Joan could do was to repeat the phrases after me in a dull flat monotone. No amount of voice work helped until there was a marked improvement in her language comprehension.

Since Joan often seemed oblivious of the speech around her, it was important to do something about directing her attention to it. For this purpose, the speech pathologist recommended that we assemble a device which consisted of a funnel attached to rubber tubing at the end of which was an ear piece. When the ear piece was inserted in Joan's ear, and I spoke into the funnel, the sounds were slightly amplified and Joan could feel the vibrations. At the beginning, I used this tube almost every day for about ten or fifteen minutes, but after several months, I reduced our use of it to once or twice a week. It was a very useful training instrument because it helped Joan to listen and to reproduce certain sounds she had not used before. The result was that she became generally more aware of speech and began to hear individual words better. This was important because Joan needed to receive all the words in a sentence in order to get its full meaning. We continued with this training until Joan began to have enough language facility to automatically supply missing words within the context of a sentence.

I read fairy tales to Joan to familiarize her with the beloved characters all children know and enjoy. They were completely without meaning to her at first, but after a while she did come to recognize some of the most popular ones and could identify them in book illustrations. The make believe world and the real world soon became separate and distinct, and Joan was able to distinguish between them in her reading.

The speech pathologist saw Joan again in January. She found her auditory memory poor and her comprehension inadequate. However, there was improvement generally, and she encouraged us to continue the same program we had been following. The resolution of Joan's problems depended solely upon the continued use of a training program tailored to fit her needs.

Joan's main difficulty this year was with the social studies program which required her to understand the significance of holidays, and to understand how they related to historic events. This proved to be completely bewildering to her, and I could make little headway now with this. Joan was just barely able to cope with practical everyday experiences in the present, let alone events of the past or the future. The concept of time; yesterday, today, and tomorrow, was barely within her grasp. The festivities around Halloween, Thanksgiving, Christmas, birthdays, and so on, were essentially incomprehensible experiences to her. She participated in the making of symbols like the jack-o-lantern, teepee, totem pole, Christmas wreath, birthday cake, and so forth, but she did not understand their meaning as yet.

Nevertheless, there was growth within this school year as evidenced by Joan's rating in the Metropolitan Achievement Tests which were administered in May of her first grade year. She scored second grade, fourth month, and the director advanced her to second grade.

Within this year, Joan's learning speed had increased, the periods of no learning had become shorter, and there were fewer regressions. We also noted a change in the quality of Joan's voice by the end of the year. It was becoming slightly modulated and softer.

Chapter 14

THE SUMMER WHEN JOAN WAS SIX AND ONE-HALF

During the summer, we moved to another house. Joan's first grade teacher offered to tutor her during the month of June when I was very busy with preparations for moving. They had about ten one-hour sessions together. The hours were devoted to remedial reading with second grade texts. There was no tangible evidence of improvement in her reading comprehension after this period was over because the tutoring was not geared to Joan's specific needs. Although her comprehension was below par for a second grader, Joan's phonetic understanding and word attack were superb.

At the end of June, the head of the speech clinic decided that work with Joan should be discontinued. He and his staff had done a wonderful job in helping Joan relate to people. They had stimulated speech, and they now wanted to see Joan develop further without assistance from the clinic. Although Joan was very inarticulate and spoke very indistinctly, both the speech therapist and Mrs. Kastein felt that speech therapy at this time was not indicated since it might inhibit a spontaneous flow of words.

During July, Joan went with the younger of her two brothers to day camp. Although it was a brand new camp experience for Joan, with a full day program six days a week, she adjusted to it immediately. I will never forget how cheerfully and happily she marched off that first morning with never a backward glance at me. The camp was very small, relaxed, and non competitive. Joan came home each afternoon, happy about her friends, the games, swimming, and all the other activities. For the first time since I had started a teaching program with Joan, I suspended the sessions entirely, and watched her grow more and more in a social sense. Her camp companions noted her poor speech, but they liked her and accepted her. She was cheerful and cooperative, and so adept in all the physical activities at camp that she had real status within the group. It was wonderful to see her so happy.

We spent August in the Adirondacks again, and we resumed the same study program we had had the previous year. This continued until the middle of September when Joan returned to school. I used our summer study time to help her with language and to strengthen her understanding of number concepts. The approach was varied, as always, and we worked hard.

At the age of six and one-half, Joan was still finding it exceptionally difficult to understand speech, and to respond to it. Those who did not know of her problem thought she was merely inattentive. It is a curious thing that through all these years when Joan's responses were far below one's expectations for a child of her age, few people suspected the existence of a problem. She looked alert, was pretty, and in recent times had become very friendly. If language deviation was noted, it was promptly attributed to shyness, parent coddling, stubbornness, lack of interest, or immaturity. Her poor speech was labeled "baby talk" and was not considered worthy of concern. Even when the problem was brought to their attention, most people dismissed me as a harsh critic of a "perfectly adorable child."

Joan could understand and respond to words only when she deliberately directed her attention to speech. To help her better grasp this difficult process, I used a method of asking Joan to repeat after me each statement or request that I made. I found this to be an important discipline because it forced Joan to make an effort to listen. I was persistent, and I detained her until she did what I asked her to do. This improved Joan's ability to focus on speech, and also improved her memory.

There was definitely language growth, but Joan's responses were still labored instead of being automatic. When I spoke to her, I could almost see the gears turning as she received the sounds, translated them into word symbols, and interpreted them into the concrete terms to which she could respond.

Joan had by now grasped the meanings of the words, before, now, later, yesterday, today, tomorrow, next week, next month, last year, the day before yesterday, the day after tomorrow, and so on. Furthermore, she could now comprehend birthday celebrations, holidays, outings, and vacations. Joan could anticipate forthcoming events and could predict the outcome of certain situations with a fair degree of accuracy. These had all been particularly troublesome areas for her.

As Joan began to understand the world a little better, she gradually began to relax. That meant that it was becoming a little easier to care for her. We were beginning to talk to each other and Joan's responses were becoming clearer and more logical. She was also becoming more reasonable about frustrations, delays, my sharing of myself with others, and so forth. Certainly her demands were still excessive, but if reasoning with her failed, I could now successfully enforce disciplines that could control much of her difficult behavior. She cared very much about having my approval.

Slowly, my husband and I began to realize that we were enjoying Joan as a person. More and more she was participating in all of our family activities, and she was becoming an enthusiastic and cooperative partner. On the occasions when she was recalcitrant, it was because she did not comprehend a particular situation and was expressing a desire and need to understand it. There was a vast difference though between her previous expressions of frustration and her present behavior. Now at last, we could calm her down because we were able to reach her with words. Joan was understanding language and the nature of communication more and more each day.

Joan was now becoming more aware of the differences between my husband and me, and she began to relate differently to each of us. She asked questions about Daddy's work, and went directly to him to have things fixed. He discovered that he had a little daughter who could be charming on occasion, and a warmer relationship began to grow between them. He enjoyed spending time with her and was delighted to teach her how to ride her bicycle and fly her model airplane. He helped her in his workshop where she loved to use his tools.

The relationship between Joan and her brothers was excellent. I marveled at the fact that they expressed no overt awareness that Joan had problems. Of course, we were discreet and never discussed Joan in their presence. Perhaps it is naive to assume that they were unaware of Joan's problems simply because they did not talk about them. I must conclude that they were either satisfied with Joan's language responses to them or completely accepting of them. They never criticized her or became impatient with her unless she angered them. In their play together, Joan's good understanding of concretes allowed her to size up a situation by using visual aids, and enabled her to come up with some kind of answer. In playing indoor games, the boys expected to make allowances for her age. They did not seem to care how generous they were. In outdoor activity, on the other hand, her skills were so excellent that she challenged them.

The brother who was two and one-half years older than Joan adored her and sought her company constantly. He went out to play with his friends only if she was occupied with me. Their communing started early in the morning and consisted of a good deal of horse play. I feel that the relationship Joan had with this brother taught her much that she could not have obtained in any other way. He taught her how to play many children's games, and together they enjoyed many children's fads. They sported Davy Crockett headgear, gyrated with hula hoops, collected baseball cards, played with tops, and so on. Joan also learned the lingo connected with these activities from her brother. It was fortunate that he could provide all this for Joan because these passing fancies are important to a child's growing up experience. Aside from being fully involved with the serious business of teaching Joan language, I, as an adult, could not possibly have provided the enthusiasm and excitement that were necessary to the enjoyment of these activities. Only children can do this for each other.

Together Joan and her brother made collections of things that interested both of them. Our son was a very imaginative child, and he shared his fantasies with Joan, apparently caring little how meagerly she contributed to them. His was an insatiable curiosity, and he took Joan along with him on his explorations into books about planets, rocks, birds, presidents, and so on. He loved learning about new things and happily talked to Joan about everything that excited him. It did not seem to bother him in the least that Joan promptly forgot what he had just told her, or perhaps, had not even understood what he was talking about. He patiently and cheerfully repreated the name of the bird or flower or whatever it was that they were talking about when it next came to their attention. The tangible benefit of this was Joan's awakening interest in books.

Joan's older brother liked her too, but he was not nearly as close to her as the younger one. The older boy was amused by Joan's impishness and sometimes enjoyed playing with her, but he did not seek out her company. The age gap of five years was too large, and they had few interests in common. He was intensely involved with his own creative and specialized activities. He did not have the carefree playfulness of the younger boy who found frolicking with Joan so delightful. Nevertheless, the older boy sometimes joined the younger children in play out of doors, and always assisted Joan in assembling a toy or game if she needed his help.

Sometimes, Joan was a nuisance, especially when the two boys were involved in some complicated project which she did not understand. When she annoyed them, they simply dismissed her. This usually made her very angry because she resented being excluded from anything. She fought to be reinstated. Since she was so strong willed, I often had to enter the fray. I was, as always, adamant about protecting the boys' rights. In time, Joan learned to use charm instead of strong arm methods in order to stay in favor with the boys. She learned how to be a spectator when they were busy, and felt tremendously rewarded when they allowed her to become their "girl Friday."

We were now approaching a more normal existence than ever before. The lines of communication were opening wider each day. The future looked more promising than it ever had. Joan's progress this past year had been so impressive that I dared hope that she could manage with less help from me in the second grade than she had received until now. I was not reckoning with the much increased demands of school and society.

Chapter 15

JOAN ENTERS SECOND GRADE

JOAN ENTERED SECOND GRADE still bogged down because of poor reading comprehension. Her general reception of language was definitely below par. However, during two or three conferences with her teacher, I received assurances that Joan was handling the work satisfactorily. Since Joan understood the nature of communication now, and had grasped the most basic concepts, the teacher thought that perhaps Joan could proceed without my help at this time. Since I had longed for the day when I could reduce the pressure on Joan and on myself, I decided that I would take her advice and confine myself to just reviewing and clarifying curriculum needs.

I drastically reduced the formal work sessions from five or six days a week to three days a week. Instead of three hours daily with as many as five or six hours on either Saturday or Sunday, we now worked only two or three hours each time. Our work sessions were limited to an examination of the work sheets Joan brought home, and I spent some time explaining the material to her that she could not grasp alone. A portion of our time was used in checking Joan's comprehension of the number concepts because I wanted to prevent rote learning. In our work together, I emphasized problem solving in an effort to improve her language comprehension, and to check her conceptual understanding. I reviewed her reading material with her and helped her with her work books. Establishing a concept was still a long hard process, but now, once it was mastered, Joan seemed to have it at her command.

However, I felt uneasy about the relatively small amount of progress Joan was making. My observation of her told me that a long road still lay before us. Each and every experience we had revealed how very limited her vocabulary was, how impossible it was for her to relate these experiences to herself, and how generally unaware of the world and the people in it she was. Nevertheless, I continued with the curtailed program. During a four month period, Joan had less structured home learning than she had ever had before. So attuned though was I to Joan's needs, that I automatically provided her with language support throughout the day even during this period.

Towards mid-year, Joan's teacher sent out an S.O.S. Joan was not keeping pace with the group during the science and social studies periods. Greater demands were being made of her, and she was having difficulty meeting them. Back to the grindstone we went. We increased the hours of home study to what they were before we cut back at the beginning of the year.

More than a year had elapsed since we had had our last interview with the speech pathologist. This in itself indicated our greater feeling of security about Joan. Until now we had felt it necessary to consult with her about two or three times a year.

In February, we went to see the speech pathologist. She reevaluated Joan and found marked improvement. However, she felt that Joan's immature responses were still a problem and recommended that we continue to try to help her become more independent. As far as Joan's comprehension was concerned, she suggested that the only way we could help her further was by continuing to use our usual teaching methods.

I realized that I would have to give Joan's world broader dimension, or she could not become successfully integrated into the society in which she was living. Joan was mastering her basic reading and number skills and was dealing well with concrete situations. However, her understanding of relationship was limited. She could relate only to those people whom she knew like her teachers, the dentist, the doctor, and others with whom she had regular contact. When she was required to establish relationships with new people, she had difficulty in comprehending who they were. This was based largely on Joan's inability to use past experiences in understanding new ones.

In school, the curriculum included complicated, abstract areas of learning. The social studies program involved a study of prehistoric man and animals. Since Joan was barely out of the woods in terms of the ordinary language she needed for day to day communication, I was skeptical about how successful I could be in teaching her the complex ideas involved in such a study.

Ordinary experiences in the present were within her scope, but she could project her thoughts to the past or to the future only with great difficulty and minimal success. I knew that before she could actually grasp the significance of a different era and a different way of living, specifically that of the cave man, Joan would have to have a much improved understanding of her own environment. This would come in time. However, we could not wait. If Joan was to continue with her chronological group, I had no choice other than to proceed with the social studies program they were pursuing.

Books, models, museum trips, and play acting gave Joan the concrete facts that she needed to acquire. She observed and recorded, to some extent independently, differences between the cave man and modern man, between prehistoric animals and modern animals. She had apparently received adequate training in noting differences because she was astute about observing detail and accurate in identification. She was currently pursuing a keen interest in animals by poring over her many animal books whenever she had the time. She proudly displayed her knowledge at the zoo by correctly identifying many animals I could not name. When this happened, she would turn to me and say somewhat incredulously, "Mommie, don't you know that?" No personal accomplishment could ever produce the pride I felt at those moments.

In terms of her study of prehistoric animals, Joan delivered her bits and fragments of information when called upon to do so. On a museum trip, she could identify the various dinosaurs, and recite very articulately that: "Tyrannosaurus Rex was the king of dinosaurs, Stegosaurus had plates along his back, Triceratops had horns, Brontosaurus ate only plants," and so on. Considering her language problems, this alone was cause for cheers. I was impressed with her performance, but I knew that it denoted little more than a good memorization of facts and a parroting of information.

Joan's difficulty with abstractions was still unresolved. Until she learned how these fragments related to her, how to integrate them in order to use them meaningfully within other contexts, how to relate them to other experiences, how to use these facts to develop an idea, how to understand a sequence of ideas, how to predict an outcome when given a set of facts, and how to reason, she was not really receiving or using language. Practically none of her experiences represented building blocks that she could use effectively in order to form a pyramid of ideas. They were merely isolated islands, almost totally unrelated to her or to each other. Somehow, they had to be woven into the fabric of her being.

Thus, the nature of Joan's language responses was essentially the same as it had always been. What existed in concrete terms—what she could see, touch, smell and taste—she understood. This was simply not sufficient any longer. Joan needed to learn how to think better, and that meant understanding abstractions. As always, the only way I could help her to deal with intangibles was to translate them, whenever possible, into tangible form. This was becoming increasingly more difficult to do because the material she had to learn was becoming more complex. After translating abstractions into concrete terms, I had to help her relate them to experiences that had already been integrated. I checked her comprehension constantly and asked her to express the ideas she had learned in her own words.

For instance, the cave man was neatly pigeonholed into a time "long ago." This was a convenient label that she quickly learned to use. What did the term, "long ago," actually mean to her? Did it mean lunch time, or when she had her bath, or when the postman brought the mail? This was about the extent of her memory and her comprehension, and since her imagination was hardly developed at all, this was as far as she could go. "How old was I when I was born?" she asked me repeatedly. To a child who could not imagine not having been here at one time, I despaired sometimes of getting across the idea of cave men and dinosaurs living millions of years before. No one, of course, can actually conceive of that in a true sense, but we do see it in a relative sense. We understand it as a vastly different era unlike anything within our present experience. We know that there is constant change.

This was what I tried to get across to Joan. I could do this only by relating the concept of change to things she could understand or had experienced. I explained to her that she had been a baby once. I showed her her baby pictures, and I explained to her that when she was a baby, she could not walk, talk, or dress herself. I compared her infancy and her growth to the infancy and development of the world. We talked on the simplest level of other changes. I described a plant growing from seed, day evolving into night, food changing when it is cooked, and so on. Very gradually, the idea began to have some meaning. However, Joan could not achieve true perspective about all of this for quite a while.

By the end of the year though, Joan did understand that cave men and dinosaurs no longer existed, and that modern man and modern reptiles have evolved from them. She began to visualize different environments and different circumstances than those she lived in. I realized this when she began to ask me whether an event or circumstance was happening now or happened long ago. The important thing was that her frame of reference was no longer limited to just one day, but was now comprised, in a functional sense, of yesterday, last year, and a time before she was born.

By the end of second grade, Joan achieved a small understanding of a society that was bigger than the family and school groups in which she lived. Now that it was getting easier to talk to her each day, I spoke to her often about a world of people with different customs, dress, language, dwellings, foods, and climates. I tried to tell her about other lands and about explorers and scientists. Some of this information filtered through, but not too much. I knew that I just had to keep on repeating the same material in as many new and different ways as I could find in order to open the doors of the world wider for her.

One important thing was evident. In contrast to the earlier periods when progress could only be measured in terms of months, now there was such acceleration in her ability to learn, that we could see progress over a period of weeks.

Also, something even more important had happened. Joan, now seven and one-half years old, was finally acting maturely enough, so that we were able to deal very well with her. My husband and I could say now for the very first time, with little or no qualification, that we were enjoying being with Joan as fully as we had always enjoyed our relationship with our sons. Through the years, we noted that as Joan progressed in her understanding, there was always a corresponding improvement in her behavior. With the passing of time, Joan was becoming more and more a person.

Since Joan achieved well in the Metropolitan Achievement Tests, scoring third year, fourth month in April of her second grade, it was recommended that she be advanced to third grade in September. Throughout the year, Joan maintained her usual academic position in the middle of an average group of fourteen youngsters. Her success in this group was amazing.

Chapter 16

SOME OBSERVATIONS ABOUT JOAN

Through the years, I made certain observations about Joan that should be recorded. One of them concerned her eyes. During earlier periods in Joan's life, I noticed that when she was in a severely withdrawn state, her eyes, which are normally brown, became lighter in color, had no depth, lacked luster, and seemed fuzzy. They had a remote look. Her responses during this time were sluggish, and she could scarcely learn anything. I had no choice other than to return to simpler material. Actually, she responded so poorly during these periods, that the time spent seemed wasted. The only reason I continued working with her was in order to maintain the work disciplines.

On the other hand, when Joan was spiraling upward in her learning, her eyes became very dark, clear, and bright. I soon learned that I could use the appearance of her eyes as an indicator, and could, with a fair degree of accuracy, anticipate the amount of contact that I would have with Joan during a particular period.

During the exciting year between Joan's seventh and eighth birthdays, I had not noticed any eye color changes. It is important to observe here that this coincided with the disappearance of the cyclical learning patterns Joan had maintained all along. There were no longer any regressions. There were only spurts and plateaus.

Another observation concerned Joan's reactions to weather. Weather conditions always seemed to affect her. On stormy, cloudy, rainy days, she seemed not to hear well. At the same time, her learning ability regressed seriously. When the weather cleared, she returned to her former level. She could hear us, could learn, and could relate.

On the other hand, there were periods of several days when Joan did not seem to hear speech at all, and there were no apparent changes either in weather conditions or in any other environmental factors. To what could we attribute these changes in her hearing? Could it have been due to withdrawal, regression in learning, inability to listen and to concentrate, inattentiveness, a hearing deficiency, or perhaps a combination of these factors? What could explain the marked differences from one period to the next, with or without weather changes? We do not know except that, as Joan's language powers grew, her responses to weather conditions and the unknown factors that were operating decreased and eventually disappeared. Joan did not have periods of "deafness" any more. This condition, too, disappeared when Joan was between seven and eight years old.

We were now beginning to see Joan react spontansously to the words she heard all about her. Until this point, she had been unable to understand our family discussions. Through no fault of her own or ours, she had been excluded from them and she had resented this. In self defense, she had responded in the only way she knew, by chanting "Ma" constantly in order to draw my attention back to her. However, now that she was at last able to be somewhat more actively involved in our general conversation, she was becoming a little less intrusive. I felt great joy when I heard her, for the very first time in her life, use words I had not taught her. She was attempting to understand independently the meanings of new words. She was trying to contribute ideas to our conversation. Most of this improved use of language developed when Joan was close to eight years old.

Joan's increasing awareness of language now enabled her to express her thoughts, feelings, ideas, and wants, to a greater extent than ever before. This together with her much improved perception made it less and less necessary for me to serve her with my eyes, ears, and mind. However, her own faculties needed to be developed much more before we could be fully separated from each other.

Despite this fine language improvement, Joan was still too dependent upon me. She continued to exhibit immature behavior such as hand clinging, following me about the house, nagging, interrupting, and so on. However, this was definitely diminishing, and we found her becoming more and more resourceful about entertaining herself and keeping occupied when I was busy. There was hopeful progress in resolving some of these behavior problems.

During July and part of August, Joan returned to the camp she had attended the previous summer. This time she went without her brother because he was joining his older brother at a sleep-away camp. She accepted this situation gracefully and hopped on the camp bus her first morning confident, secure, and happy.

Joan was a fine camper in every respect. Again, she was liked very much by both the children and the counselors. Her skill in sports was excellent, and she was sought after as a team mate. When she learned how to swim well, she was overjoyed. She loved the water.

As usual, Joan had difficulty communicating with the children, but she managed far better than she had the previous summer. The other youngsters did not make any issue about Joan's speech. To the best of my knowledge, no critical remarks were made to her. I checked this with the counselors, and also observed Joan very carefully for any signs of problems. Joan herself, thus far, had never indicated that she was aware of any difference between her speech and that of her contemporaries. I think this was largely due to the fact that she was not yet perceptive enough to make such an observation.

As time passed, Joan's language comprehension, voice modulation, and speech continued to improve. However, we felt that the progress she made in speech and voice did not correspond to the improvement in her language understanding. Her inflections and articulation were still poor. She did not always use all of her consonants, and some of her vowels were still distorted. We observed that she did not react to bells, sirens, and high pitched musical notes.

An investigation of Joan's hearing seemed indicated, so the speech pathologist referred her to the Speech and Hearing Clinic at Columbia Presbyterian Medical Center where an otologist examined Joan's ears—the results were negative—and an audiologist evaluated her hearing by administering a series of audiometric tests. The results revealed a loss in the high frequencies. In the low frequencies, her hearing was grossly within the normal range. Unfortunately, Joan could not at this time benefit from the use of a hearing aid because she could not tolerate it. My husband and I were disappointed because we thought an aid might help Joan respond even better to voice and language training. For the time being, the matter was put aside.

Joan and I did no work during the camp season, but when it was over, we began to prepare for third grade. Now, for the first time since I had started working with Joan, I felt that I was merely tutoring her. This was a vastly different process from the one we had been involved in until this point. To me, Joan now represented a normal student who still needed extra help and drill with her school work in order to maintain a good level of achievement. Never again, from this point on, did I ever feel that we were crossing uncharted, un-explored areas of her mind. Joan was finally using all of her senses, albeit some more competently than others. Joan could obey directions, make requests, ask intelligent questions, communicate better with people, and "tune in" more and more on what was happening in the world about her. The one area where Joan still needed to make con-siderable progress was in becoming more independent of me, but we noted that she seemed to need me a little less each day.

During the summer afternoons and on weekends, we went to the beach and many interesting places. Joan was now a lovely companion and we enjoyed being with her tremendously. She was now able to give us what every child can give to receptive parents; a new look at old things. Through her eyes we were learning things that only a child can teach. The animals in the zoo had funny habits, the shells on the beach roared in our ears, and the birds had colors we had never seen before.

Chapter 17

JOAN ENTERS THIRD GRADE

In september, joan, who was now almost eight years old, entered third grade. She had a very fine teacher who agreed to give me all the assistance I might need in order to help Joan have as happy and productive a school year as possible. The curriculum seemed very advanced, and I was apprehensive about how Joan could handle the language arts and social studies programs.

In October, we had another consultation with the speech pathologist. This was our eighth thus far. She found that even though Joan was still having great difficulty with abstractions, her comprehension and behavior had improved considerably. Since her test results indicated that Joan was functioning well, she recommended that we give Joan more leisure time in which to develop her own interests and follow her own inclinations. She felt that Joan's attitudes about herself and about all her relationships would proceed on a healthy basis only if she were allowed to develop more independently. The speech pathologist noted that Joan had advanced sufficiently so that she could continue to develop language by herself. She also felt that Joan could probably manage her school work with a much reduced tutoring program.

My husband and I wholeheartedly agreed with the speech pathologist's point of view. We had, through the years been unhappy about the pressures we had had to exert on Joan, but we had had no choice. Now we welcomed the opportunity to remove most of them, but we wondered if this course of action was justified. It seemed to us that Joan still needed a great deal of support.

With these doubts in our minds, we again reduced the program of tutoring just as we had a year before, to three times a week for two or three hours each time.

After several weeks, it became apparent that Joan was making far less progress than she had been making in recent months. In fact, she was struggling so much with the increased demands the school was making that I simply had to return to a more intensive program.

My husband and I felt justified about doing this because we were reasonably certain that Joan would fall short of fulfilling her potential without our continued assistance. We felt that only a continued effort could bring Joan to the level where her comprehension would be good enough for her to work well independently. Our own assessment of her excellent progress thus far convinced us that she would achieve academic independence in time. However, we knew that Joan was still some distance from that goal.

We certainly acknowledged the fact that Joan's environment would be healthier if she were free of work pressures. However, we questioned how happy and fulfilled she could be as an adult if she were not able to make the fullest use of her resources.

Actually, we had no reason to be concerned about Joan's emotional health. Our relationship was excellent, and Joan expressed a great deal of love and warmth for both of us. Assuredly, she was excessively dependent upon me, but how could it be otherwise considering the nature of her problems all these years. What was pertinent now was the fact that her dependence was diminishing almost in direct proportion to the degree of language understanding that she was achieving. In those areas where she was fully competent, she acknowledged no decisions other than her own.

Joan seemed somehow to be aware of what was happening to her, not in an articulate sense, but in a way that permitted her to accept without complaint, a program that was intensely demanding. How else can we explain her fine cooperation through the years? She was far from being a submissive child. Any intrusion upon what she considered to be her rights brought forth a show of indignation. It was only when working with me that she yielded to enormous pressures.

Our work together was, at first, confined to helping Joan with her assignments. These studies exposed areas that needed exploration and we often went far afield. This year, Joan's projects included a study of Japan and Scandinavia. The skills and methods that Joan had acquired the previous year served her well when she studied Japan. She could observe differences in customs, food, dress, and facial characteristics. In connection with this, she learned more words and had interesting new experiences. She ate in a Japanese restaurant, sitting Japanese style on cushions, and was served by kimono clad Japanese girls. Many times after that, Joan ate with chopsticks, singled out oriental people, and found Japanese imports at home and in stores.

When she went on to the study of Scandinavia, she was able to contrast the American and Scandinavian cultures. Always enthusiastic about food, she heartily enjoyed a smorgasbord feast in school. Since we love Scandinavian furniture and art, Joan was able to find Scandinavian imports in every corner of our home. We read stories about foreign children and learned about their schools, games, and holidays. Joan could identify with them.

We used maps constantly, and when we talked of a particular country, city, river, or mountain, Joan found it independently on the map. She enjoyed this aspect of our work very much.

Joan was exhibiting the eager excitement of a young child who has just become aware of a great, big, wide, wonderful world. She was enthusiastic and curious. The stories in her texts stimulated her to think, and she asked pertinent questions. We could make substantial progress because she was now able to apply past learning experiences to new material. For instance, when we read about the Vikings, she could compare them to the pirates she already knew about. In discussing whaling, she comprehended this activity because she already knew about fishing. When we talked about the fiords of Norway, she related them to the bays, islands, peninsulas, and so on that we had discussed already. She knew something about the forces of nature that had created them.

Each of these subjects stimulated long discussions about related matters. We went off on many, many tangents. Often I could not get past one sentence in Joan's required reading assignment because it triggered other thoughts that had to be explored in order to give her a more comprehensive understanding of what we were talking about. I saw gaps and rushed in to fill them. Joan wanted to understand what we were talking about, and she was receptive. One of our difficulties now was that Joan's memory was still not good enough, and I had to repeat much of the material. She could not remember facts unless they related to her in a meaningful way.

At the beginning of the year, I started using the Gates Peardon *Practice Exercises in Reading* and the McCall Crabbs *Standard Test Lessons in Reading* to help Joan improve her reading comprehension.

They were excellent because they were geared to her particular needs.

We spent a good deal of time on science, Joan's favorite subject. I used the Singer Science series and many supplementary science books. We set up experiments and Joan displayed good logic in trying to predict what the results would be. I found her reading nature books and acquiring information I had not taught her. Nothing highlighted the scope of Joan's progress so much as this observation. Joan was, at last, learning independently. If only I could make some significant progress in improving her reading comprehension, our work would be finished essentially.

During the course of this third grade year, I again strongly emphasized the learning of arithmetic concepts and the solving of problems. I felt that if I could help Joan develop her ability to think logically, and if she could learn to handle the reading and solving of problems, there would be a carry over into her reading skills. Working on this premise, I devoted a large part of our work time to arithmetic. The amount of concentration required for problem solving is so great that she could not allow herself to drift away. The logic inherent in arithmetic is very exact, and Joan was able to perceive this. Her progress in this area was remarkable. She learned how to deal with abstractions, and mastered one number skill after another with relative ease.

I observed after a while that Joan was better able to concentrate on her reading lesson. However, her progress here was slow because language still presented problems for her that could only be solved by an increased understanding of words. Creative writing was very difficult for her, and she wrote very poor compositions. They displayed little imagination or skill with words.

I was excited and happy during this period because I enjoyed "educating" Joan. She was eager to learn and each day was productive. I saw growth constantly. In an effort to help Joan achieve the finest understanding of her environment that she was capable of, I explored each subject with her with painstaking care. In doing this, I found that I myself gained new insights. The world acquired exciting new dimension in many ways. Both of us were learning. The give and take of my relationship with Joan was finally beginning to balance out.

Shortly after Joan was eight years old, she finally succeeded in staying dry throughout the night. We had made fruitless attempts to train her to use the bathroom at night. She had tried to cooperate, but had not known how to. When we discussed the situation with her, all she could say was, "I don't go to the bathroom because I don't understand the feeling of having to go. Explain it to me." No matter how hard I tried to explain the nature of the pressure to her, I could not get it across. We became discouraged. We were looking ahead to the summer when we were planning to do some touring, and we knew that we could not go unless this problem was solved.

Having exhausted the usual methods of training, we introduced an electric signalling device which warned Joan when she started to wet her bed. After using it three or four times, Joan responded. I think her reaction was so swift for two reasons. One was that she hated the bell and wanted to get rid of it. The second reason was that she now perceived, for the first time, the connection between the pressure and the act, and was able to respond. Whatever it was, from that time on, Joan had complete control.

Joan's social development was proceding well. She understood and observed most of the social amenities. She had friends in school. Her speech had advanced to the point where everyone understood her, and she communicated freely with the children. Although it was still a labored process, she managed in a completely unself-conscious way to say whatever she wanted to say. At home, we found her to be cooperative, cheerful and enthusiastic about everything.

What was still lacking was the sophistication appropriate for her age. She exhibited her immaturity in many small ways like attempting to be the center of attention and displaying impatience over delays. However, she was not too different in this from a good number of youngsters of eight or nine, and indeed, some of her controls were far better than those of some of her contemporaries.

Joan completed her third grade with a score of fourth grade second month on the Stanford Achievement Test. She took the examination with the same group she had been together with all along. She maintained her usual position in the middle of the class of eighteen youngsters.

During the summer, Joan returned for the third time to the same day camp she had been attending. She was delighted to meet some of her old friends, and she again enjoyed her camp experiences. Joan continued to progress beautifully in her swimming, and she learned how to dive. Her coordination in the water was superb, and she had remarkably good endurance. I listened to her in amazement when she came home and explained to us, in words, the theory of proper breathing while swimming, and again, in words, explained the various kinds of swimming strokes. On Sundays at the beach, she undertook the job of improving my faulty breathing and faulty strokes. During all this, she was as sweet and patient as could be. Had we not indeed come "full circle?"

Camp was so much fun for Joan that she stayed on for eight weeks. When the camp season was over for all three children—the boys also had attended camp again—we took a trip to Washington, D.C., Williamsburg, Virginia, and Jamestown, Virginia. It was a fine experience. It helped Joan realize that this is one big country with most of the people in it alike in appearance, speech, dress, and manners. She absorbed, retained, and used what she saw. She was eager to learn and was full of questions. We found her ready to participate in all our discussions.

Actually, we had undertaken this trip very hesitantly because we were apprehensive about what Joan's reactions would be to the long car rides, shared sleeping arrangements—she had always had her own room—new foods, many strangers, and discomforts of all kinds. Our fears were unwarrented because Joan was able to take everything in stride. She adapted herself to all conditions, understood what we were doing, anticipated the events we described to her, and enjoyed the many new things we were experiencing. Although the sights themselves were very new and exciting to my husband and me, what was most thrilling was the fact that it was, at long last, possible to take such a trip with Joan and enjoy it.

This was the first summer that Joan had no structured learning program whatsoever. I tried, of course, to make our trip as meaningful as possible by explaining as much of it as I could. We were reliving our country's past, and Joan began to develop some small sense of history as we went along.

Chapter 18

JOAN ENTERS FOURTH GRADE

O NE DAY IN EARLY September, Joan related a dream she had had the night before. She had this dream after she had repeatedly asked me for permission to walk the five or six blocks to school by herself each day, and I had denied her request.

"I was running to school by myself and a car stopped with a lady in it. She said to me, 'Do you want a ride in the car?' I said, 'No thanks. I can walk by myself.' Then I ran some more. Another lady stopped and asked me, 'Do you want to ride in my car?' She had two kindergartners in her car. I said, 'No thanks. I can do it all right.' I was running some more and then another car came with a man in it. He asked me, 'Do you want a ride?' and I said, 'No thanks. I can do it all right. Don't bother me.' Then I ran some more and I was at my school."

Although the school was so near, either my husband or I had always driven her there and back. We had not permitted her to walk because the route was along a narrow country road with no sidewalks, and we felt it was dangerous. I explained this to Joan, but she assured me that she could take care of herself. She persisted and even enlisted a teacher's aid to plead her cause.

I was in conflict about this situation because I knew Joan to be responsible and trustworthy now. I was certain that she would obey the limitations I would set forth. I also realized that she was approaching the age of nine, and wanted and needed to have more independence. Yet I could not say yes because I was afraid she might get hurt.

Finally, I promised her that when she entered fifth grade, I would consider her old enough to take on this responsibility. As of the day I told her that, she relaxed. From time to time, she spoke of the happy day when she would go to school by herself.

Joan's learning curve was now a steady upward one with just the usual variations we all experience. There was growth from day to day, and we could see the gap between her and her classmates becoming smaller.

I continued to tutor Joan every day for two to three hours after school in order to keep the level of her work high and to help her further with her abstract thinking. Although there was tremendous improvement in her reading comprehension, it was still not good enough. She was a very fast but very inaccurate reader sometimes destroying the meaning of a passage by skipping or substituting words. Even when she read coherently, she had difficulty, because she could not distinguish between essentials and trivia. When asked what the significance of a passage was, she gave the details, but usually missed the essence of the story. On the other hand, when I read to her, she was able to listen and understand considerably more than she did when she read independently. I continued using the Gates Peardon and McCall Crabbs material to help her resolve the reading difficulties that persisted.

Another manual that I found particularly helpful this year was the *Practice Workbook of Reading*. It contained very short stories of a wide variety, and each story was followed by questions designed to test comprehension of the article. Besides helping Joan with her reading skills, they provided her with information on a vast number of subjects. Such stories as Why Kill The Bat, Volcanoes, The Deer Like Salt, What Becomes of Worn-Out Money, Where Did the Pilgrims Settle, and so on, enlarged Joan's scope of knowledge tremendously. This was clearly reflected in her fine achievement scores in social studies and science at the end of the year. In addition, the two or three paragraphs that covered each subject gave Joan a small understanding of how thoughts are put together in clear, concise, logical order. She gathered the facts readily enough, but got bogged down when she had to draw conclusions or offer explanations that were not stated for her in the article. For instance, a story might describe the manufacture of shoes and discuss a machine that tested the durability of the leather sole. When I asked Joan why the manufacturer tested his product, she was unable to tell me that he had to have a good product if he hoped to sell it, and he could only tell whether it was good if he checked it. I had to tell her this, and she understood my explanation in this particular situation. However, she could not apply this kind of reasoning and logic to the next story because she had still not developed an ability to think abstractly. Helping Joan to learn how to sort and select pertinent facts for the purpose of constructing an idea was extremely important. This was a major area where she still needed tremendous help.

I proceeded with this by asking her to explain much that was ordinary and commonplace. For example, I asked her why we use transparent glass for windows. She answered that all windows are made of glass. She said nothing about the fact that this kind of glass admits light. Yet in discussion, she could readily describe the difference between translucent and transparent glass. To the question of why roots grow down, she would answer, "That is how a plant grows," even though during a science lesson a short time before, she recited that plants need water and minerals in order to grow, and they get what they need through their roots in the soil. If I asked Joan why we have daytime and nighttime, she might say that this is the way the world is made, instead of telling me about the rotation of the earth on its axis. Yet, she had a very adequate understanding of the universe and could explain the relationship between the earth, the sun, and the moon.

It was obvious that Joan had amassed an impressive amount of information at this point, but I knew that a mere recitation of facts was not desirable. Unless she learned to use them correctly, I had produced nothing more than a well trained robot. This I wished to avoid.

Teaching Joan how to think could not be confined only to our work sessions. This was simply not enough. I found that I was constantly prodding Joan into giving me explanations of everything in her environment. The result, in time, was more penetrating questions from her, and greater agility in coping with mine. The quality of her responses improved. She became more logical, and began to express herself more creatively. This greater astuteness was soon reflected in her school work.

The fourth grade this year was so large that it was divided into two classes, and Joan was put in the more advanced of the two groups. She was aware of her position and rose to the challenge. It was a challenge indeed because she was still one of the youngest of a total of twenty-one students.

Science continued to be Joan's first love. We used the fourth grade text, *Science in Your Life,* as well as many other fine science books. Based on our concentrated work and her improved understanding,

Joan's world was expanding. She learned about space, the earth, the sun, the moon, the planets, weather, magnetism, electricity, insects, birds, the tides, the human body, hibernation, and so on. We did interesting experiments together, and as the year advanced, Joan became increasingly more excited about what she was learning. Since she was still not sufficiently articulate, she had some difficulty expressing her thoughts, but her teachers felt that she could contribute satisfactorily to classroom discussion.

The social studies program was very exciting, too. For the first part of the year, the class studied Ancient Egypt. Joan had by now, developed enough of a sense of history and a clear enough understanding of her own culture to begin to observe the contrast between ancient and modern times.

Of inestimable value were the museum exhibits of tombs, mummies, sarcophagii, relics, crafts, reproductions, and so on, which helped her to understand the role of the archeologist and the importance of his findings. We tried to read the hieroglyphics on the walls of the tomb, and I was delighted with Joan's imaginative responses. She observed a great deal, and finally began to try to relate what she was learning to what she already knew. However, since the material was not associated, by and large, to what she experienced in her daily living, she needed much interpretive help.

I gave Joan a great deal of assistance with the vocabulary, the idioms, and the concepts in her reading text. I noted a marked contrast between the way she dealt with words now and the way she had before. There was also a measureable improvement in her ability to deal with abstractions. Although still very literal, she was beginning to grasp the concept of symbolism as expressed in the Ancient Egyptian culture.

We contrasted the religious beliefs and practices of the Egyptian and modern religions. We compared our writing with hieroglyphics, our leaders and laws with Egyptian Pharoahs and their decrees, our architecture and materials with Ancient Egyptian building crafts. We talked about many, many things. There was an exchange of ideas and a deluge of questions. Even though Joan's imagination was being stimulated, and she was responding in a more creative way than ever before, her learning process was still very difficult, and the information was instilled only after laborious hours of work.

Next came the study of Greece, and a whole different world opened up for Joan. Again the museum visits provided superb visual material. With much help from me, Joan was able to understand her history text.

Then, one day, she brought home a series of assignments in Greek mythology, and I threw up my hands in despair. How could I ever hope to teach her these fantastic myths? Incredibly, she took to them like a duck to water, and was able, with coaching, to retain the names of the gods, and understand the relationships, the roles, and the intrigues of these mythological characters amazingly well.

For another assignment, Joan had to read a simplified version of the *Odyssey*. At first, I regarded this as impossible, and meant to deal only very casually with it. However, when I saw how well she grasped it, and how much she enjoyed it, I applied myself to it seriously, and tried to make it a rich experience for her.

Joan enjoyed reading science books because they dealt so much with concretes. I often found her browsing, in her leisure time, through her numerous reference books like the excellent How and Why series which included such titles as *Rocks and Minerals, Sea Shells, Birds,* and *The Human Body* amongst others. There were fine Giant Golden Books like *Facts and Figures, Birds, Geography, Dinosaurs, Science,* and so on, which she also enjoyed very much. The Allabout series which consisted of such books as *Volcanoes and Earthquakes, The Ice Age, Strange Beasts of The Past,* and many others, fascinated her. Joan liked accumulating interesting facts to share with me and her brothers.

For fiction, Joan selected books far below her grade level. For the time being, I encouraged her to read anything at all because I felt that it was extremely important for her to experience maximum success in connection with her independent reading. I refrained from testing her comprehension of these books, feeling completely satisfied when she told me that she had finished a particular book and had enjoyed it.

In a January conference with the speech pathologist, she observed that Joan's behavior was more mature and found her responses generally to be consistent with her expectations for a child of nine. Noting her good progress and satisfactory school achievement, she again urged me to curtail the tutoring program. She felt that now that

Joan was functioning well within the norm, she would develop a greater feeling of adequacy and more independence if she had more freedom to develop her own interests.

In the past, whenever I had curtailed the home teaching program, I had found the results unsatisfactory in terms of Joan's academic achievement. As a result, I had always found it necessary to return to a fuller schedule. With this in mind, I was skeptical about whether Joan could really manage with less support from me than I had been giving her until this point. Nevertheless, I was willing to try it again, and once more I limited the program to three times a week. Joan did indeed seem much happier with the greater freedom she had. She promptly joined an afternoon sports group that met once a week and spent a good deal of time playing out of doors. She loved having the companionship of children, but when that was not possible, she was very resourceful about entertaining herself.

I had several conferences with Joan's teachers. She had a departmentalized program in which she had different teachers for different subjects. Unanimously they reported that they were satisfied with Joan's social adjustment. They found her to be dependable, self confident, and cooperative. She was interested in her school work, had good study habits, and tried very hard to achieve well. In her relationships with her peers, she handled herself capably. She had a sense of humor and was fully a part of all the sassing and teasing that went on back and forth among her classmates.

One teacher questioned Joan's reluctance to seek help from him when she was confused by a lesson, but understood that her pattern of relying on me was long established, and that it would take a while before she could go to others for assistance. When assured that her teachers were always prepared to discuss her problems with her, Joan began to express confidence in them too.

Joan's teachers also discussed with me her apparent preference for outdoor activities with the boys in her group. We all understood that this was due, to a large extent, to the fact that she was such a good athlete, but it was probably mostly based on her lack of identification with the things that interested girls like dolls and clothes. The girls' imaginative excursions were too fanciful for her to comprehend, and their fast never-ending chatter left her somewhat bewildered. I observed this on several occasions when I accompanied four or five girls on a school field trip. Joan could not compete with them, so she avoided them. She knew that with the boys, the less talk the better. Only "hits and runs" counted with them.

However, Joan managed very well when rainy weather confined the children to indoor activity, and she was grouped with the girls for games like checkers, Scrabble, Monopoly, or any other current favorites. Incidentally, these were games I had never taught Joan. She had learned them from her brothers and her classmates, and she now played them competitively and well.

The academic reports from her teachers indicated good progress in some subjects and a need for further help in one major area. Specifically, the mathematics teacher told me that she was achieving well with the advanced group. She understood all the required concepts, solved problems, and did computations accurately and easily. She was also doing well with the social studies program. In her science class, Joan was an enthusiastic pupil and understood her work here too. The French teacher reported that Joan was making satisfactory progress in her class. I was thrilled to hear this because her achievement here reflected solely what she had learned in school. I gave her no assistance with this subject at home.

The English teacher was less satisfied with Joan's progress. She recommended that I help her with her creative writing skills. Here, Joan was achieving less well than in other areas because her vocabulary was still too limited, and she did not yet understand well enough the nature of self expression either in speaking or in writing. The teacher suggested that I give Joan a word or phrase like Thanksgiving, the letter, birthdays, my pet, and so on, around which she could build a story. After two or three abortive attempts at this, Joan adamantly refused to continue these writing exercises. I temporarily abandoned them with the idea that we would resume them when she was more at ease with words.

Joan started doing reams of crossword puzzles. She used some excellent ones published by Treasure Books. She also played word games that we either bought, borrowed from television, or invented. Since the whole family enjoyed these, Joan always had enthusiastic opponents. Our three youngsters often kept themselves amused and busy with these games on long trips in the car.

We really became a very word conscious family. As a result,

Joan's vocabulary increased a good deal this year. She loved building up her stock of words, and could usually give me two or three synonyms for the words she knew. Her spelling skill was excellent. Her reading comprehension was advancing, and I noted that she tackled new reading words very ably. Joan could read words after she had been exposed to them only once. I no longer gave her the meanings and explanations for words or sentences. I expected her to decipher them within the context of the sentence, or to look them up in the dictionary. Joan's language power increased every day.

This year, Joan learned about parts of speech, and she handled her grammar lessons independently because she was learning this aspect of her work so well within the classroom situation. This was also always true of spelling.

It is fitting to observe here that the level of Joan's work had advanced to the point where I was often inadequately prepared to teach her. At times I was only able to keep just one step ahead of her. Just when I was feeling most insecure because I had forgotten practically all my geography, history, and science, could scarcely recall the grammar rules I had learned so long ago, and was struggling with the New Math, Joan had a dream. In her dream, I died. She cut my head off and tried to place it on her own shoulders. However, she could not do it because it did not fit. When I asked her why she wanted to put my head on her shoulders, she answered, "Because you are so much smarter than I am." I immediately reassured her by telling her that she had a very good head resting upon her own shoulders. This dream made me feel very sad and introspective.

In many, many ways, this unusual little girl had provided me with tremendously meaningful experiences. I certainly would not have elected to have had the problems associated with her growing up, but since I had had no choice in the matter, I could do nothing but accept the reality of the situation. I worked hard to do all I could to help Joan fulfill her potential. In the course of this, I found myself enriched in many respects. We had grown, she and I, in countless ways; she towards greater maturity and academic achievement; I in acquiring some understanding of her, the nature of her problems, and the differences in development that can exist amongst children.

Joan was fun to be with. Everyone found her friendly and outgoing. Although shy in new situations, she related well with most people.

She identified with me in some ways in my role as a woman. She spoke of having her own family when she grew up. When I worked in the kitchen, she was eager to assist me and usually acquitted herself admirably whatever the chore was. I sometimes thought she was over confident when she offered to do something that defied my efforts, but a tight jar cover, a balky vegetable shredder, or a nut grinder about to come apart all responded to her excellent mechanical know how.

Although not particularly interested in gardening, Joan often joined her father and helped him with the fertilizing, sowing, raking, and weeding. Endowed with remarkable endurance, she worked long after her brothers were completely exhausted.

I taught Joan how to sew and crochet, and she learned very quickly. However, she was not sufficiently interested in these activities to perfect her skills. She much preferred baseball, kickball, dodgeball, bike riding, or skating.

The relationship between Joan and the younger of her two brothers continued to be a very loving one. Their play ran the gamut from wild physical activity to quiet talks together. I found that after an hour or two of play with him, Joan was happier and more responsive than ever. He was close enough in age to her to share some of her interests, and with his very bright and creative mind, he stimulated her in innumerable ways. I often heard him say to her, "Did you know that . . . .?" "How do you think . . . . ?" "What would have happened if . . . .?" or "Why did this happen to . . . .?" Joan's responses to him were surprisingly good for the most part.

Joan's relationship with her older brother was also excellent even though he was rarely her playmate now. She was considerably impressed with his skills with electronic equipment, and acknowledged the fact that he was very clever and well informed by always suggesting that we go to him when we were stumped for an answer. A dream that she had revealed how she felt about him. In her dream, three robbers came to our house. She was frightened and called to her older brother for help. He quickly subdued all three of them. She called the police who took the intruders away. Obviously, her brother was a hero to her. This dream reflected her admiration for him and her sense of security with him.

We were a happier family now. Joan still depended upon me to make certain decisions which I felt she could handle herself. However, she was certainly growing more independent every day.

Early in the year we took Joan on a trip to a museum where she heard a lecture through a set of earphones, and we observed again that when sounds were fed right into her ears, she apparently was more attentive. We discussed this with the speech pathologist who arranged another hearing test for Joan. The result showed no change in her hearing, but this time the audiologist felt that Joan could tolerate an aid, so one was prescribed for her in March, nineteen hundred and sixty-three.

Joan accepted her hearing aid very quickly when we explained its purpose to her. It was only during the first month when she was becoming accustomed to it, that she sometimes rejected it. After this initial period of adjustment, Joan took full responsibility for wearing it all the time.

The only change that was immediately apparent to us was that Joan now reacted to certain noises that she had not seemed to be aware of before like the hum of the refrigerator motor, the buzz of the washing machine timer, and so on. We knew that some time must elapse before we could determine how helpful this device would really be for Joan.

Actually, during the course of this year before Joan ever received her hearing aid, her speech had gradually become more fluent, better enunciated, and more correct grammatically. The quality of her voice had improved tremendously. By the time she received her aid, it was rather well modulated and expressive. Obviously, her auditory awareness had increased.

From the time Joan was a small child, we had considered the possibility that she had a peripheral hearing loss. However, we always felt that if one existed, it probably was a relatively minor one and could not begin to explain her history of severe language impairment. If this were not so, how else could we reconcile our observation that from early infancy Joan's response to sounds of varying volume demonstrated that she had more hearing than her response to words indicated. We felt that Joan always had sufficient hearing to permit language to be received if no other problems had existed.

We had consistently observed that as Joan's language comprehension developed, she heard more and responded better to words coming to her from far and near. We believed that this was the crux of the matter. Therefore, we did not expect the hearing aid to accomplish much more than focus her attention on speech.

During this year, significant changes occurred which indicated how much better Joan was tuning in. For several months, she had been listening and participating in conversation around the dinner table. However, she had always withdrawn when the words and ideas were unfamiliar or too advanced for her to comprehend. More recently, because of her considerably improved language comprehension, instead of withdrawing, she was insisting upon an explanation for those things she did not understand. She was conceiving of it as her due to be included in all we said and did. She demanded her rights in a constructive sense as a member of the family rather than as a nagging infant seeking attention.

We approached the new year with more confidence than we had ever had before.

Chapter 19

THE SUMMER WHEN JOAN WAS NINE AND ONE-HALF

This was a wonderful summer. Joan spent July in the same day camp she had been attending for several years. Then in August, we went on a five and one-half week trip through our New England States and the Maritime Provinces of Canada. The boys were back again in camp for the summer and joined us for the last ten days of our trip.

Camp provided Joan with the opportunity to be with her friends, to improve her swimming and diving, to go horseback riding, to enjoy a variety of athletic activities, and to participate successfully in a dramatics program.

The highlight of the summer, though, was our trip. Besides enjoying many new experiences, Joan delighted in having my undivided attention, and as much of her father's as he could spare from his driving. Perched on the back seat of the car with her face thrust between us, she bombarded us constantly with questions. With the boys away, Joan was really the "queen bee." Very much aware of her still-existing need to have help in understanding her environment, I tried to include her in everything we saw and did. However, my husband and I needed some privacy. We had decisions to make, plans to talk over, or merely a desire to sit quietly with our thoughts. We found that Joan chattered so incessantly that it was impossible to ignore her. In desperation, I often had to ask her to stop talking so much. When I did, I recalled those years when I had yearned to hear her speak. Begging her to "cease and desist" now filled me with emotions I can scarcely describe. Who can know what it meant to me to turn to her and ask her to stop talking so much? Every time I did, I felt as though I were committing a crime.

We were able to discuss this question of privacy with Joan. She understood and responded respectfully. She began to sense when it was appropriate for her to participate and when it was important for her to be unobtrusive. After a week or two, we found that Joan could relax in the back of the car with a coloring book or games for as long as an hour or two without interrupting us. Her behavior generally reflected greater confidence, security, and awareness.

On this trip, Joan amply demonstrated the fantastic progress she had made already. For instance, on a guided tour of Acadia National Park in Maine, she showed an avid interest in everything that the Park Naturalist Guide was talking about. At the end of his delivery, he asked for comments and questions. Joan did not hesitate to participate, and before a group of about one hundred and sixty people, she asked two or three questions clearly and intelligently. She then listened respectfully to his answers. True, her questions were necessary largely because she had missed some of what he said, but they were pertinent. Throughout, she seemed self possessed, and I was very admiring of her.

The trip proved to be very varied and exciting for all of us. Joan participated in all our experiences, and even contributed to the making of decisions. She met new people with ease, adjusted nicely to unfamiliar foods, and accepted the discomforts of travel which sometimes included undesirable accomodations. She learned a great deal about the history and geography of the area through which we traveled.

When the time came for the boys to join us for the last ten days of our trip, Joan looked forward to the reunion. Away for eight long weeks, the boys had much to share with us, and together they pushed Joan into the background. This was actually a much healthier and far more realistic situation for her than the one that had existed for the previous four weeks. She reluctantly abandoned her queenly role, and accepted the fact that the boys would now also help make decisions, claim a share of our attention, and interrupt her monologues. Joan had matured a great deal this summer and was a happy little girl.

Chapter 20

JOAN AT THE AGE OF TEN

J OAN'S TENTH BIRTHDAY WAS a very happy occasion. She was excited for days before, but exhibited admirable self control. As usual, she had a little party in school, and fulfilled her responsibilities as class hostess graciously.

At home we had our customary festivities, and Joan waited patiently until dinner was over to see her gifts. With great anticipation she opened them, and in dramatic contrast to former years, examined each one with deliberate care before going on to the next one. Since her greatest interest was in making things, we gave her an abundance of craft materials and projects.

It had always been our custom to give each child an increase in allowance for the coming year at birthday time. Quite unexpectedly, and to our great delight, Joan asked us a few days before her birthday what her new allowance would be. This was the first year that she really understood the significance of an increase. Money now had the special meaning for her that it has for all of us. She recognized it as an important commodity that could disappear if not handled wisely. I began to observe signs of thrift when she was making decisions about buying things for herself or presents for others. She was developing good judgment about its use, and did not hesitate to spend it when necessary.

Now, too, in line with her better understanding of the use of money, Joan began to resent paying the fines I imposed on her for infractions of rules. Heretofore, this particular discipline had been without meaning to her. Even though she had not appreciated its significance until now, I had perpetuated it with her in fairness to the boys for whom it had always been an effective restraint.

Joan achieved well throughout her fifth grade year. Her intellectual growth was continuous and most satisfactory. However, the curriculum needs were very demanding, and I still had to assist her a good deal. She proceeded very well with her mathematics, spelling, grammar, and vocabulary study, but the social studies program which dealt with ancient history through the Roman Empire was so compli- cated that I had to help her with it. In science, I gave her minimal assistance, and she learned the required concepts satisfactorily.

This year, I actually could have let Joan proceed independently. She would probably have managed to learn her assignments, but the level of her achievement would probably have been lower. The prob- lem was that her reading comprehension was still below par. Also, she was still not picking up words sufficiently well to indicate that ade- quate growth would proceed without the assistance I was giving her. On the contrary, when I did ease up, Joan had difficulty with her learning and became discouraged. Since she liked studying and achiev- ing, it seemed important to help her be successful.

Besides helping Joan with her homework assignments, we con- tinued using the Gates Peardon and McCall Crabbs materials. Joan read books which we discussed in detail. Crossword puzzles, always a favorite activity, continued to teach Joan many new words. We still played different kinds of word games, had fun with homonyms, and interpreted idioms, proverbs, and mottos. Joan genuinely enjoyed expanding her vocabulary.

In the latter part of the school year, a situation came to my atten- tion that I think could only have occurred with a child who has had language problems. I received this report from the classroom teacher who had witnessed the incident. One day in school, two boys hurled epithets at Joan without any provocation from her. The teacher as well as the other girls in the class were repelled by the unusually foul words that the boys used. When Joan did not respond to them, the teacher was amazed at what he interpreted as her self control. Sad that Joan was so abused, and severely shocked at the vile language he heard, the teacher proceeded to scold the boys. Relating this story to me a few days later, he described her behavior as "incredibly stoical." He brought the situation to me because he was fond of Joan and was concerned lest such an incident be potentially harmful to her.

I told the teacher that Joan had briefly mentioned the incident to me, but had dwelt mainly on a description of his anger. Although she had sensed that these two boys, who had been in conflict with her and everyone else in the class throughout the year, had been unjusti- fiably malevolent towards her, she had not realized how seriously they had maligned her. The boys, unbeknownst to them or anyone else, could not succeed in arousing Joan's ire one bit because she simply did not understand what their words meant.

When I explained to the teacher the reason for Joan's apparent phlegmatic response, he was amazed. Although with her practically a whole year, he had never been aware that she had any language limitations. Knowing that most children during the course of growing up are exposed to vulgarisms, he had assumed that Joan was familiar with those words too.

I continued to try to make further effective inroads into resolving what remained of Joan's basic language problems. She was unquestionably an intelligent child, and the progress she had made thus far was fantastic. I felt that if I gave her a little more help, she would very soon use her potential more fully and independently.

Joan's usual pattern of language response seemed to be to translate each word or small group of words into her own terms as we do with a foreign language that we do not know too well. This was a slow process, and as a result, there was delay in both her reception and expression of language. Her particular responses reflected, of course, her special language problems, but I felt that certain habits had probably been established over the years that served possibly to perpetuate these patterns.

In order to help her react more spontaneously to language, I began to present to her, a series of very simple statements containing either concrete or abstract ideas. I wanted her to tell me whether my statement was true or false. I would say, for instance, "I am wearing a green dress," "It is raining outside," "Today is Tuesday," and so on. I deliberately used extremely easy words, because my purpose was not to test knowledge, but to evoke quick responses. Initially, I gave her time to deliberate, but then I speeded up the process to make her respond more quickly. What I hoped to stimulate was the kind of automatic response we all make to language. She rose to the challenge with gratifying results.

It is impossible to determine what factors, in such an intensive teaching and learning relationship as existed between Joan and myself, were responsible for the growth we saw. All that can be said is that by the end of the year, Joan made excellent progress in language comprehension.

What was not so readily amenable to improvement was Joan's

expressive ability. Although considerably improved over the preceding year, it was still not adequate. As she spoke, I could see her searching for words, putting them together in a deliberate way, and even then, sometimes saying things she did not mean to say.

To help Joan express herself more imaginatively and more fluidly, I asked her each day to tell me a story about any subject she chose. I provided her with a long list of suggestions. Invariably, her stories were personal, simple, and logical. Although they revealed her still inadequate use of language, they represented enormous growth when compared to a year before when she could not do this at all satisfactorily.

There were other methods I used to assist her in expressing herself. One was to ask her to free associate. Her responses were amazing. She used both concrete and abstract terms, responded very quickly, and showed imagination and humor. It was here that she demonstrated the considerable scope of her vocabulary. It is interesting to observe, however, that although she could automatically produce words in response to a stimulus like the preceding word, she could not readily put them together to form sentences for the purpose of constructing a story. I encouraged her to talk about experiences and to read aloud.

As a result of all these efforts, we began to note steady improvement in Joan's ability to express herself. She became more imaginative and articulate. The progress she manifested made us feel very confident that Joan could become fully expressive and fluent before long.

At the end of the school year, I attended a class production of an operetta and heard Joan deliver its lengthy introduction to an audience of about one hundred and fifty children and adults. She projected her voice well, spoke clearly, and was well poised. She was duly congratulated by the teachers and pupils for a good performance. Joan was very pleased with all the approval she received. This increased her feelings of confidence in herself.

After Joan had worn her hearing aid for about a year, my husband and I were better able to evaluate it. Our opinion was that it was valuable in helping Joan hear certain speech sounds all the time that she had previously heard only through the tube. As a result, her articulation improved considerably.

We felt that Joan heard words better when she had her aid on. I could always tell when she was not wearing it because I had to repeat so much of what I had said. When she put it on again, her attentiveness increased and she communicated better.

We felt also that Joan understood more with her aid on. Her responses improved because the words were more distinct. Unlike children who have no language impairment, Joan still could not fill in words that were omitted. She needed to hear and understand all the words in a sentence in order to comprehend what was said to her.

However, we felt that if Joan had not been provided with a hearing aid, her progress would not have been seriously impeded. In our judgment, Joan's progress depended primarily upon the development and training of language. As her comprehension improved, she heard more. It was as simple as that.

Joan's own reactions to her hearing aid reflected her excellent understanding of what it accomplished for her. She was delighted with the fact that she could hear certain sounds now all the time. She recognized it as an important aid in speech training. When she first got it, our own enthusiastic endorsement of it made her feel as if it were a vital instrument that she could not possibly manage without. However, she soon achieved proper perspective about it. She acknowledged that it assisted her, but realized that it was not indispensable. After several months, she became quite casual about the whole matter. On several occasions, she told me that her battery had needed replacement in school, but that she had not bothered to replace it with the spare one she had in the teacher's desk, "because I heard very well without it." This was probably true because Joan was certainly becoming more "tuned in" to speech.

Although the aid became relatively less significant as Joan's language comprehension improved, we still felt that there was important justification for its continued use. It focused her attention, provided her with sharper hearing, and undoubtedly lent greater clarity to her world.

The school year ended with cheers from all who knew Joan. Her teachers considered her well prepared to proceed into the sixth grade. Her progress in learning, self expression, and articulation had been magnificent.

In July, Joan went to a day camp for a month, and then we all

went on a six and one-half week trip out West to visit the National
Parks. It was a completely happy vacation for all of us. Joan observed
and understood more than she ever had before.

Chapter 21

CONCLUSION

Joan is now eleven and one-half years old and is in the sixth grade. Physically, her development is excellent. She is tall, healthy, and very well coordinated. On the athletic field, she is outstanding. She is pretty with light brown hair, expressive eyes, a ready smile, and an infectious laugh. Her voice is well modulated, her articulation is satisfactory, and she has good inflections in her speech. Joan is adept, as always, in the use of her hands, and is clever about solving mechanical problems.

Of our three children, Joan is the most outgoing. She loves having new experiences. She enjoys meeting new people and relates well to them. Although she still prefers being with boys on the ball field, I have recently heard her talking about girls and showing some interest in doing the same things they do. For instance, I find her fussing with her hair and expressing opinions about her clothes. I think that as she accepts herself more and her self image improves, she will identify more fully with girls. We are encouraging this as much as possible.

Generally, Joan has insufficient confidence in herself, and as a result, may hesitate to do something she can actually handle well. However, in some areas like sports where she succeeds, she is very self assured. She has drive and makes a persistent effort to improve in those endeavors where she feels she is not capable enough. As she succeeds, her confidence grows. We hope to see her make progress here.

In school, Joan is a completely responsible child. Her teachers tell me she is self-disciplined, industrious, and dependable.

I find her reliable at home too. She usually does her chores like making her bed, helping with the dishes, and keeping her clothes and room tidy, but shows some healthy resistance to this on occasion. She will often volunteer to assist me with my household tasks if she is not too engrossed in her own activities.

Joan is fun-loving and vivacious, and she has a nice sense of humor. My husband and I feel that she is a happy child. We find her even-tempered and adaptable. On occasion, when she sulks or is resistive, it is usually with just cause. She is sensitive and if dealt with fairly is a very easy person to get along with. If anyone tries to trespass upon her rights, she defends herself heroically. She handles disappointments well.

Recently, my husband and I made our plans for the coming summer. We decided to send Joan to a sleep-away camp for the first time. This expresses more eloquently than volumes of words our feelings of confidence in Joan. We hope that it will foster greater independence in her.

Before making the decision, we discussed this plan with Joan. Her spontaneous reaction was a forlorn, "Oh, I don't want to leave you, Mom," but with practically the same breath, she excitedly asked, "Will you give me enough stationery so that I can write home a lot?" She expressed this ambivalence several times during the next few days, but then seemed to accept the idea of going away fully. She started to make all kinds of plans for camp and asked many questions. We know that she will have a good deal of adjusting to do, but somehow I do not anticipate that she will experience an undue amount of homesickness. I, on the other hand, miss her already.

The fact that we were ready to make such a decision, and that Joan could accept it, offers as good an indication as any I could give of how far all of us have progressed.

We see Joan now as a basically healthy, normal child. In most aspects of her living she is doing well. However, she still needs to make more progress towards achieving greater maturity. The question arises for my husband and me as to whether we have contributed to the immaturity Joan manifests.

When we examine our roles with relation to Joan, we realize that the very nature of her problems in the past has made us tend to be very protective of her. We have always made decisions concerning her with a considerable amount of caution. For instance, each spring when school enrollment time has come, we have had to decide whether to transfer Joan to the public school or keep her where she is. Admittedly, the school she attends has important advantages such as small classes, an advanced academic program, and so on, but our public schools are excellent too. In the early years, we felt that Joan needed the small group situation that this private school provided. However, in the past three years, objectively we could safely have made a decision for either public or private school. We have always elected to keep the status quo. This judgment was based largely on the fact that Joan was progressing well in her school, and we were reluctant to venture into the unknown with her. In two years more, Joan will enter high school, and we are not considering anything but the public school for her then.

Has this caution and protectiveness contributed to Joan's immaturity? We think not. We feel that the major reason Joan does not have a maturity appropriate for her chronological age is that she still has an insufficient grasp of abstractions and some difficulties yet in integrating experiences. Over the years, an arduous training program enabled her to advance to the point where she was able to achieve insights into how people live, work, and play together. Concurrently there was emotional growth. We have always observed that when there was an increase in Joan's language comprehension, there was a corresponding increase in her level of maturity. This correlation still exists today. As she continues to grow language-wise, we feel confident that she will become more independent.

When we pause to ponder over Joan's past, we recall that she did not really "come to life" until she was approximately three and one-half years old. Those first years when vital language development normally occurs was a period of near "nothingness" for Joan. If we were to subtract those three and one-half years from Joan's chronological age, we could not fail to be tremendously impressed by the gigantic scope of her progress.

How do we assess Joan's language development now? I would say that her vocabulary is superior to that of most children her age. She is now picking up words from all sources. When she speaks or writes, her choice of words is almost always appropriate. I note a certain timidity on her part as she starts using a new word and a shy twinkle of awareness as she watches for my reaction to a particularly apt use of one. I was impressed and openly admiring one day when I heard her say, "that man is *expectorating* in the street," and "he *obviously* has no manners." A short time later in a restaurant I enjoyed hearing her say that a portion of food was "*unusually* large," and she did not "*particularly* want that much." Going home she said, "It is *extremely* late." In a discussion about crime she spoke of someone being "*annihilated*." These are just a few examples of the kinds of words she is now using. It is truly astounding to us that she can now use such terms considering her initial difficulties.

It has become second nature for me to define any new words I am introducing to Joan, the first time I use them. Within the context of a sentence, I give her the synonym immediately after I say a new word as in the following. "This is *precisely* (exactly) the right time to do this," "Do not *detain* (keep) me now," "This is very *significant* (important)," "I do not like to *deceive* (fool) anyone," and so on. I also make a deliberate effort to use those words again very soon.

In addition to the impressive vocabulary that Joan has amassed, she is showing steady improvement in her comprehension. Until recently, she had confined her reading to science and very simple story books, but now she is independently reading and enjoying some excellent children's books by E. B. White, Hugh Lofting, Laura Ingalls Wilder, A. A. Milne, and P. L. Travers amongst others. While her understanding of these classics is good, it still does not have sufficient scope and depth. This makes me feel that I should continue to help her, at least a little while longer, with the language needs that still persist. While her grasp of concretes is excellent, she still has her usual difficulties with abstractions. I help her with those intangibles-words, idioms, and experiences-that she cannot fathom herself. The process is relatively easy because Joan's thinking for the most part is logical and organized now, and she has developed a very good memory. We can communicate readily because her labored search for words is finally over. Joan is speaking spontaneously.

I would also like to help Joan express herself more creatively and imaginatively in her speaking and writing. Recently there has been encouraging progress in this area. One day, for instance, something her father said triggered an imaginary journey to the moon and back with a fictional character that was purely a product of Joan's fantasy. Her father encouraged her, and they made several delightful "flights of fancy" together. This is an entirely new kind of experience for Joan. She continued this gay banter with her father for a few days more. During these conversations between them, Joan had a sparkle on her face indicating that she was enjoying herself. She displayed humor and whimsy throughout.

Joan's achievement this year in school has been most satisfactory. On her Stanford Achievement Test, Intermediate II, Form X, she scored at grade level and was in the sixtieth percentile of her group that ranged intellectually from low average to genius. Generally speaking, the over-all progress that Joan has made this year has been the most outstanding that she has ever made. From day to day now, we see significant change in her understanding and response.

We now envision goals for Joan that we never dreamt possible. We see no reason why she cannot some day soon enjoy all the subtleties of relationship, express herself creatively, enjoy travel experiences to the fullest, read and enjoy great books, and appreciate the theatre, music, poetry, and art.

My involvement with Joan all these years has been very intense from time to time and I have wondered whether I have satisfactorily fulfilled my responsibilities to my sons. This has been of concern to me. A pause now and then for introspection has always given me the reassurances I have needed. The very nature of Joan's problems usually demanded priority attention and consumed a great deal of my time, thoughts, and energy. In the first few years, she never for a moment let me forget her extraordinary needs, and I was always acutely aware of my special responsibilities to her. However, I tried never to lose sight of the fact that Joan was no less and no more important than anyone else in our family. The special attentions she had to have when her comprehension was very limited and her behavior was so difficult were reduced as more and more language was established. I then expected her to conform to the same disciplines as her brothers did. To have handled her as a privileged person even though she continued to have special needs would undoubtedly have created problems for the boys, and could possibly have produced additional ones for Joan. It was important to help Joan understand and accept the patterns of living within the family.

Fortunately, the boys were very calm and undemanding children. Over the years, we observed them developing in a seemingly effortless way. Somehow, we must have met their individual needs because today, at the ages of fourteen and sixteen, we find them to be secure, happy, well adjusted boys. They have proper values, excellent

relationships with their peers, and outstanding school achievements. In their relationships with us, with each other, and with Joan, they seem to reflect the love and respect we tried to give them. They have confidence in themselves and in us. They share their ideas and feelings freely.

In a recent discussion with the boys, I asked them specifically how they felt about my tremendous involvement with Joan in the past. They looked a little surprised at the question, shrugged their shoulders, and answered that they had never felt deprived because of the special attention Joan had received.

Until about four years ago, we had not explained the specific nature of Joan's problems to the boys. However, we had always shared with them the fact that her needs were exceptional. Now in our talk together, they expressed the idea that they would have resented having me as involved with them as I had been with Joan since they never had any special needs and never wanted special care. I realized, of course, that they were expressing their point of view within the context of their present understanding of the situation. They scarcely had memory of the feelings they had when they were very small.

As I write about the boys, I recall with gratitude that during those bleak days when I was sure I was in a permanent stalemate with Joan, they sustained and helped me in innumerable ways. Talking with them, reading to them, taking them to the playground, or playing games with them were very satisfying experiences for me and for them. I found that the boys gave me confidence in myself because they were developing so beautifully. They also gave me insights I could not otherwise have achieved into how children think and feel. They provided me with guide lines that could direct me with Joan. Most of all, they gave me respite from merciless hours of toil, with goals so distant, I often despaired of reaching them.

I reflect with interest about how Joan's emotional experiences while growing up differed from those of the boys'. When Joan was three and one-half years old, she functioned on a level far below her chronological age, and was able to make very little independent language progress. During the course of the years, we followed a program of habilitation that was geared to helping her develop her potential as fully as possible. Those years were difficult for her in many ways. She was denied freedom, was harnessed to a tremendous work load, and was subjected to enormous pressures. Her behavior initially was so unrelated, hostile, and excessively egocentric that she could hardly function. When given freedom, she abused it. She did not understand limits. We found it absolutely necessary to use controls of different kinds until she could understand herself and her environment. We are convinced that if we had not proceeded as we did, Joan could not have developed into the responsible social being she is today.

The boys, on the other hand, thrived in a relatively free atmosphere. They understood their environment and seldom were in conflict with it. We felt it necessary to impose some limits upon them in order to create a realistic structure within which they could develop securely. They understood the limits and accepted them. Within this framework, we did all we could to encourage them to develop as individuals.

The contrast between the ways in which Joan and her brothers developed intellectually is equally marked. The boys' learning advanced in a completely normal way while Joan's progress, even with help, was scarcely perceptible for a long time. As long as the boys were provided with a setting that encouraged investigation, exploration, manual activities, a learning of skills, and the development of the senses, they went on independently to form concepts and understand abstractions. They could learn words. Intellectual growth proceeded because they could observe, comprehend, recall, and integrate new concepts. They could build a pyramid of ideas. They could respond to the stimuli that they received from their senses. They could comprehend meanings from experiences and remember them. They could use all their faculties effectively. They could anticipate action and reconstruct experiences. They could form logical hypotheses. Just as there was no need to exercise any undue control over their behavior, so was there no need for us to exert any teaching pressures upon them. We knew that pressure could be a tension producing force and we assiduously avoided it with our sons.

Why then, did we use it with our daughter? We did because her situation was entirely different. Even though exposed to stimulating experiences of infinite variety, to people, conversation, books, or any other learning media, she was unable to use them except in the most limited way imaginable. We feel that the tremendous teaching pressures we imposed upon her were absolutely vital, life giving forces. Without them, she probably would not have learned to use her senses effectively.

She would not have developed adequate language, and she would not have integrated experiences sufficiently into her life to be able to use them as stepping stones to further learning. My husband and I feel certain that Joan would be living a very sad and limited existence today if we had not helped her in the specific way we did.

Although I usually tried to be patient with Joan, I did not always succeed. The responsibility of caring for her often became onerous, particularly when regressions occurred or progress was too slow to quantitate. There were periods when Joan's behavior was so intolerable that I felt hostile towards her. In the early years, when I understood far less than I do today about her development, I sometimes condemned her as a willful, destructive child. Even when I found a rationale for her behavior, I could not accept it with equanimity. However, in spite of her remorseless hounding of me, I felt a very special closeness to her which expressed itself in different ways. For instance, I felt great anguish when she hurt herself even a tiny bit. I was afraid to let anyone care for her other than my husband or myself. On the few occasions when I spanked her, I felt extremely contrite. Finally, when I began to understand the nature of her problem a little, I grew still closer to her. I was always willing to invest much energy in meeting her needs, but when my work began to bear fruit at last in terms of Joan's magnificent progress, I could easily have mustered twice the energy I was expending if she could have used it.

The teaching sessions were a constant challenge and were ever changing. They had to be. No established methods of teaching could be used because we were crossing uncharted paths. I would use the books and materials as a jumping off point, but then I improvised all kinds of techniques and methods to accomplish my purpose. If one approach did not work, there were literally hundreds of others to explore. Essentially, I had to be very flexible in my teaching and let the situation dictate the course or direction I would take. During this time, I feel I learned a great deal myself about how learning actually takes place.

I found out very soon after I started to teach Joan that our regular sessions alone would accomplish relatively little. They were productive but insufficient in terms of Joan's tremendous needs. Initially, minimal progress was made during these periods because she could not learn fast enough. What was far more important was to maintain constant contact with her throughout every waking hour of the day. This literally meant stopping practically any activity I was engaged in to teach her a concept or word with which she was struggling. Over the years, it required a power and persistence which, if translated into energy, could probably have moved a mountain.

The motivation to make such a directed effort was manifold. First and foremost was the fact that my husband and I loved Joan very much. We felt tremendous responsibility for her. As she advanced from abyssmal confusion to substantial awareness, we felt extremely grateful that there were answers to her problems. We also had the strong conviction that Joan was endowed with good intelligence and would not be able to achieve her potential unless we made these deliberate efforts.

I have often stopped to consider how Joan has reacted to the intensive program she has had to live with all these years. In some way that I cannot fathom, Joan has always seemed to understand my desire to help her and has always been most cooperative. Until recently, she submitted herself regularly to three, four, and sometimes five or six hours of continuous study with little protest. Now, she is ambivalent about the study situation because the scope of her interests has widened. In the last three years or so, she has groaned when I have taken out her books, but has yielded after some procrastination. She sometimes tries to work out deals with me whereby study time is shortened if she achieves well. She is pleased and works diligently when she has made what she considers a good bargain. The study sessions are demanding, but stimulating for both of us. While there is discipline, there is fun and informality too.

Since I have brought such enormous pressures to bear upon Joan, I have wondered if it has negatively affected her attitude towards me. As well as I can determine, the relationship between us is extraordinarily good. Joan is certain of my love for her, and returns it a million-fold. She is a sweet, affectionate person and is kind in every way.

Occasionally, Joan has healthy outbursts of anger during which she may exclaim, "I hate you," but I find that they are always triggered by something specific I have either said or done that she is displeased about. The flare-up subsides almost immediately and excellent relations are quickly restored because Joan does not harbor resentment.

When Joan is dissatisfied with a particular situation, she agitates for what she considers to be her rights. She is learning the advantages of being diplomatic in her approach to people, and generally does an effective job of "lobbying" for what she wants.

My husband and I feel that Joan is a basically well adjusted child who is making the necessary progress towards greater maturity and towards gaining more confidence in herself.

Joan has made my life very busy, but she has also made it meaningful in many ways. Amongst other things, she has taught me tolerance and forbearance.

Many people have been involved in our efforts to help Joan, and to all of them, my husband and I express our everlasting gratitude. We are especially indebted to Mrs. Kastein for the professional skill with which she has guided us. Her sincerity, optimism, and encouragement sustained us throughout. As I write this, I recall the answer she gave us at our very first meeting in response to our anxious question as to when, if our training efforts were successful, our problems with Joan would be resolved. She told us in a confident tone that if we gave Joan the right kind of help, her problems should be resolved sufficiently by the time she was ten or eleven, so that she would be indistinguishable from other children who have had no impairment. And so it is! Hers was a prediction born of the special knowledge and experience she possesses and which she made available to us. We always felt that Joan's life was important to her, and that she wanted to help us make it as full, rich, and happy as possible. We thank her.

The task of training Joan was gargantuan. It would have been impossible without my husband. Through these difficult years, he gave me confidence and support. Whenever I needed him, he was there to listen and to sympathize. He helped me clarify my thoughts and encouraged me to try new approaches to Joan's complex problems. He uncomplainingly accepted limited companionship from me during those times when I was fully occupied and concerned with Joan. If I ever succeeded in lowering his spirits, he rallied quickly and lifted me with him. When I think back over the years, I feel his loving presence by my side, and know beyond a doubt that he gave me strength and stability. Without these qualities, I would have failed everyone.

I close this narrative with much emotion. It has at times been very difficult for me to relive the memories of the past and to put them down on paper. I have often been tempted to lay down my pen, but I have not done so because I think it possible that this "Story of Joan" may give to some the hope and guidance they seek in their own efforts to help their "Joans." Our Joan's story is not yet ended, but, to us, the future looks very bright.

PART THREE

EPILOGUE

Shulamith Kastein

EPILOGUE

Joan has passed her eleventh birthday and has reached puberty. She had shown continued progress each time she was seen for re-evaluation and the gap between her functions and dysfunctions had been steadily narrowing.

During the past seven years Joan has been seen at various intervals. However, at no time did she show such marked improvement as between the ages of ten years and nine months and eleven years and two months. When she returned for re-evaluation in December 1964 at the age of eleven years and two months, after a five month interval, it was obvious from the moment she entered that a decisive change had taken place.

Joan was now spontaneous and verbal. She was free from her previous taciturnity; free to reach out, to relate, to react to and express humour and imagination; free to take up a challenge and assert her opinion.

Joan's hearing level had remained the same. She wore her hearing aid concealed under her curls and when asked indicated that she felt comfortable about it. Her voice was good, her speech adequate except for somewhat flat sibilant sounds. Under stress, she still reverts to speaking with her jaws closed, causing mumbling.

In informal conversation, Joan communicated verbally and with ease. For the first time there was no indication whatsoever that this eleven year old girl was in any way different from any other child her age. On language tests it was necessary to probe in order to find evidence of the residual language disorder and central nervous system deficit: Joan still had difficulty in comprehension of abstract concepts, though now on a higher level. She still had difficulty in using verbal concepts that involved abstract thought processes; she showed limitation in recall of material orally presented when the answer depended on abstract generalization; and there was some difficulty in silent reading comprehension because of the same problem. Visuo-motor functions were below expectation, as seen on the Bender

153

Gestalt Test and emotional immaturity and lack of sex identification
was reflected in her drawings of a person (see Appendix, Figures 8
and 15).

In order to determine whether the gains in language functions
were parallelled by gains in intellectual growth, another formal psychological evaluation was arranged.

In March 1965, Joan was tested by the same psychologist who
had examined her two years before. She was eleven years and five
months old at this second evaluation. The findings corroborated the
gains observed in the language evaluation:

> In general, Joan's test responses were entirely acceptable for her
> age. She has excellent memory and well developed perceptual sensi-
> tivity. She showed sharp visual attentiveness to details which, ac-
> companied by extreme eagerness to succeed, produced superior achieve-
> ment in tests which depend on these capacities . . . . Thus, on two sub-
> tests (Information and Picture Completion) she performed at the level of
> fourteen to sixteen years! On a Picture Vocabulary Test she obtained a
> test age of fourteen years and six months.
>
> These superior scores compensated for some less than adequate
> performance in handling the more abstract verbal conceptual material
> which still presents problems. It is very interesting to observe the
> balance that has emerged between Joan's performance and verbal
> scores, each of which is now within normal limits. I can see the effec-
> tiveness of her excellent "work style," an eager persistent struggle for
> success—in combination with her perceptual analytic skill . . . . If she
> did not have the motivation or the perceptual acuity there would not
> have been the superior performance that did emerge. This is a dramatic
> example of the development of balancing compensation for learning diffi-
> culties.
>
> Another area of competence is arithmetic. Joan handled the arithmetic
> problems with less confidence than skill, timorous about the results,
> concerned about failing. Nevertheless, her score was on the level of a
> sixteen year old.
>
> Although there has been steady progress over the last few years in
> intellectual development, there has not been a parallel progress in
> emotional growth. Joan's drawing (see Appendix, Figures 9, 10) of a
> lady and a man represented inflated, childlike figures with almost no
> sex distinction. Two years ago, her figures were one inch high and
> squeezed together in the upper corner of the paper. In neither instance
> do we have projection of comfort or understanding of one's self. Since
> Joan has just reached her menarche and is eleven and a half it is not
> possible to separate the more customary problems of adolescence from
> her individual personal growth problems . . . . Her growing years have
> not been easy ones and it is small wonder that she feels troubled about
> her adequacy.

Joan's academic achievement, the results on both the language as
well as the psychological tests, point toward the tremendous progress

this child has made. They also support the initial assumption of the high intellectual potential, now reflected in her superior ratings on some of the psychological tests. It is this potential which enabled her to benefit to such a high degree from the special training program she has received. It also made it possible for her to learn to compensate for the deficit in neural organization. Since she has achieved the normal balance between performance and verbal test scores, it is safe to say that the gap between her functions and dysfunctions is closing.

Joan has repeatedly expressed the wish to go to college and there is no reason why she should not succeed. Joan's future holds the same opportunity, the same hopes and fears as does the future of any other child her age. As with many other children, the selection of a career will have to be planned with consideration of her strongest abilities, such as mathematics and science, and with minimal demands with regard to verbal conceptualization. Her training has equipped her with excellent study habits and perseverance and the acquisition of good perception and memory. If she can be helped to progress independently, without the mother's tutoring, and to gain emotional growth, she should attain the goal she sets for herself.

No other child will ever be exactly like Joan, will have the identical genetic or intellectual endowment, the identical sensory reactions, the same drives and personality traits, the same history of impairment or the same dysfunctions. Nor will another child be born into the same family or have the same mother. No other child will respond to therapeutic management in just the same way Joan did. Success and failure in habilitation must be considered in the light of these differences.

Children as a rule cannot be studied under laboratory conditions. Conclusions, therefore, must be based on these individual cases who present the characteristic manifestations and reactions found in a large clinical population. Follow-up studies on these children allow meaningful comparisons between those non-verbal children with central nervous system deficit who were diagnosed at a young age and received therapy, and those who were seen at various age levels without having had the benefit of diagnosis or treatment, nor indeed parental realization of what was wrong with them.

There is no "control" for Joan. We do know, however, the progressive devastating effect neurological disorganization and lack of language development may have on children when they are seen for evaluation at a later age. At that time, secondary mental retardation or secondary emotional disturbances may be found which would preclude habilitation or limit its effect. Joan might have been one of those children.

The case of Joan demonstrates what has been observed clinically: The importance of early diagnosis and early therapeutic management, including parent counselling and an individual training program.

Since emotional as well as functional adverse compensatory mechanisms develop early in the growing non-verbal child, it is important to investigate failure to develop verbal communication as soon as it is suspected. Allowing for individual differences in the rate of growth, most children use words at about twelve months of age, and phrases at about twenty-four months of age. Any difficulty in comprehension or in the use of words at thirty months, or any time thereafter, should be investigated. At this early stage of development the causes for the deficiencies in language development can usually be detected by exploring discreet elements of language such as peripheral, central and psycho-motor functions, intelligence and emotional adjustment.

Early language evaluation is imperative also because the differential diagnosis is the only basis for therapeutic management. This management is most effective at a time when the growing organism is physiologically geared for the development of speech. This optimum time of preparedness may then be utilized to train in functions which the child cannot develop unaided. This was done in the case of Joan.

Many non-verbal children with central nervous system deficit need therapeutic management to help them achieve organization of sensory perception as the basis for their future development. What this therapeutic management has done for Joan is evident from her achievements and is borne out by standardized test results.

Another reason for the importance of early diagnosis and treatment of the non-verbal child is the change in psycholinguistic functions which occurs between the ages of about six and seven years. While before this time language development seems to evolve through sensory motor integration, after this critical time, perception and the ability to learn academic skills depend upon the previously acquired verbal language. It was the good fortune of Joan to have received training before this critical time. This enabled her to develop and progress and assured her continuous intellectual growth.

Joan's entire life experience is summed up in a dream she had after she was told that the story she knew her mother had been writing was about herself. Mrs. Trace kindly permitted me to quote Joan's account of her dream. I cannot think of a better, more illuminating ending to the history of this sensitive, intelligent, exceptional child, than her own words:

> "I had a happy dream last night. I dreamt I went to school and told Kate that my mother had written a book. I said to her, 'Do you want to congratulate her?' Kate answered, 'No.' I went over to a boy. I don't know who it was, and said to him, 'My mother wrote a book. Do you want to congratulate her?' He said, 'No,' too. Then I realized I hadn't used the proper words when I asked them, so I went up to another child and said, 'My mother wrote a book. Please congratulate her,' and he said, 'Yes.' I felt so proud."

APPENDICES

Appendix 1

DRAWINGS

Joan's records of the Goodenough Drawing of a Man Test and the Bender Visuo-Motor Gestalt Test.

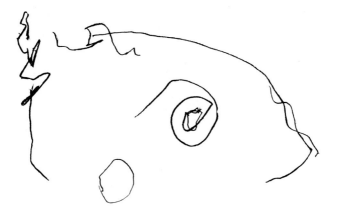

DRAWING 1. Drawing of a "man" at age four years and four months.

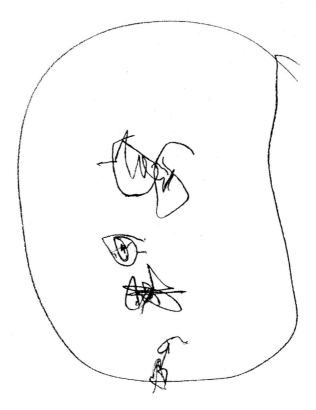

DRAWING 2. Drawing of a "man" at age four years and seven months.

DRAWING 3. Drawing of a "man" at age four years and ten months.

DRAWING 4. Drawing of a "man" at age five years and six months.

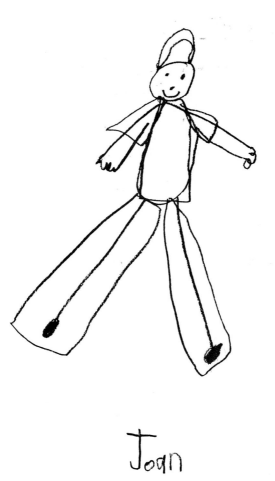

DRAWING 5. Drawing of a "man" at age six years and three months.

DRAWING 6. Drawing of a "girl" at age eight years.

DRAWING 7. Drawing of a "girl" at age ten years and nine months.

DRAWING 8. Drawing of a "girl" at age eleven years and two months.

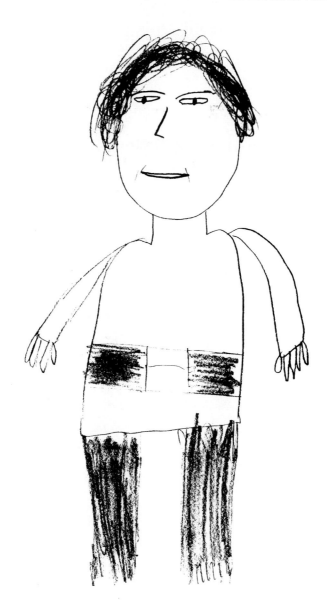

DRAWING 9. Drawing of a "lady" at age eleven years and five months.

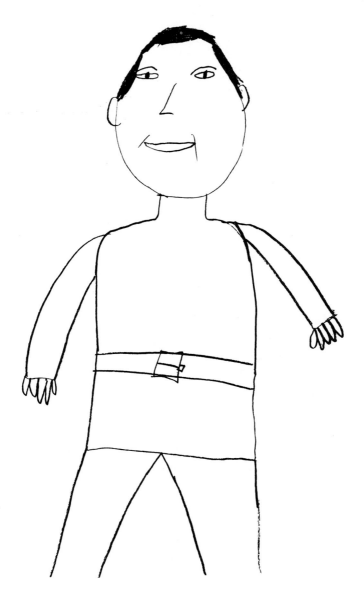

DRAWING 10.   Drawing of a ''man'' at age eleven years and five months.

DRAWING 11. Reproduction of the Bender Gestalten at age five years and
          six months.

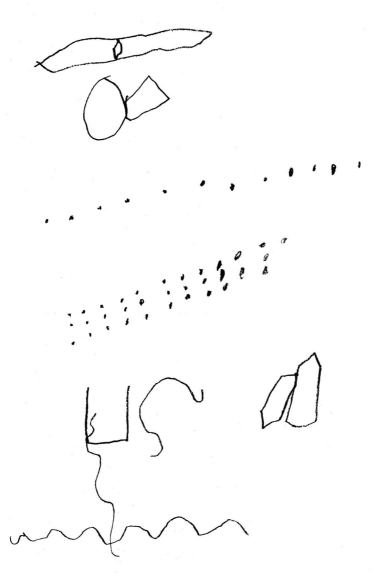

DRAWING 12. Reproduction of the Bender Gestalten at age six years and three months.

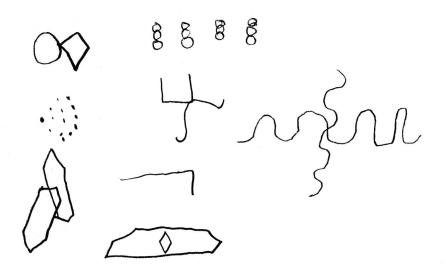

DRAWING 13. Reproduction of the Bender Gestalten at age eight years.

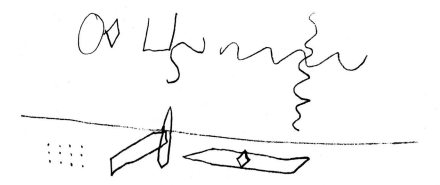

DRAWING 14. Reproduction of the Bender Gestalten at age nine years and
three months.

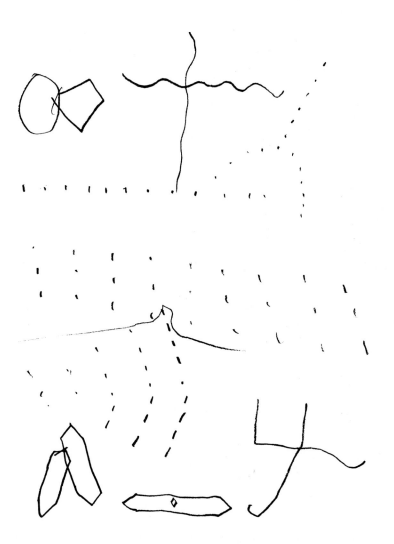

DRAWING 15.   Reproduction of the Bender Gestalten at age eleven years and
two months.

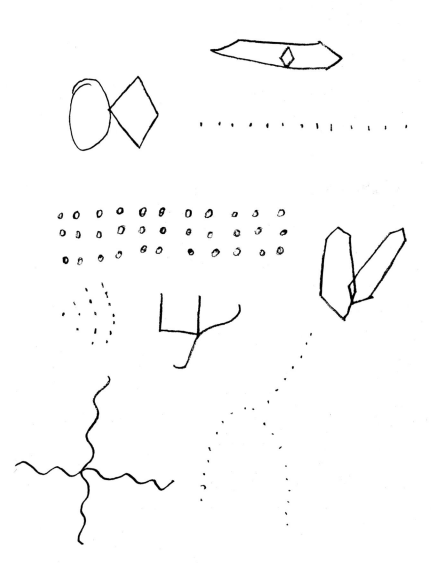

DRAWING 16.   Reproduction of the Bender Gestalten at age eleven years and
five months.

Appendix 2

SELECTED READINGS

Bangs, T. E.: Evaluating children with language delay. *Journal of Speech and Hearing Disorders, 26:*(1), February 1961.

Barry, H.: *The Young Aphasic Child.* Washington, D. C., Alexander Graham Bell Association, 1961.

Beebe, H. H.: Auditory memory span for meaningless syllables. *Journal of Speech Disorders,* September 1944.

Bender, L.: *A Visual Motor Gestalt Test.* New York, American Ortho-Psychiatric Association, 1938.

Biber, G.: *Children's Drawings.* New York, Bureau of Educational Experiments Bank Street Pamphlet No. 6.

Church, J.: *Language and the Discovery of Reality.* New York, Random House, 1961.

Fraiberg, S. H.: *The Magic Years.* New York, Charles Scribner's Sons, 1959.

Freud, S.: *On Aphasia.* New York, International University Press, 1953.

Froeschels, E.: *Kindersprache und Aphasie.* Berlin, Karger, 1918.

Gesell, A., and Ilg, L.: *Child Development.* New York, Harper, 1949.

Goodenough, F. L.: *Measurement of Intelligence by Drawings.* Chicago, World Books, 1928.

Hardy, W. G.: On language disorders in young children: A reorganization in thinking. *Journal of Speech and Hearing Disorders, 30:*(1), February 1965.

Junker, K. S.: *The Child in the Glass Ball.* New York, Abington Press, 1964.

Kastein, S.: The different groups of disturbances of understanding language in children. *The Nervous Child,* January 1951.

Kastein, S., and Fowler, E. P., Jr.: Language development in survivors of premature birth. *A.M.A. Arch. Otolaryngology,* February 1959.

Kastein, S., and Fowler, E. P., Jr.: Differential diagnosis of communication disorders in children referred for hearing tests. *A.M.A. Arch. Otolaryngology, 60,* 1954.

Kastein, S.: An analysis of the development of language in children with special reference to dysacusis. *The Special Child in Century 21.* Seattle, Special Child Publications, 1964.

Kilpatric, W. H.: *Foundations of Method*. New York, The MacMillan Co., 1936.

Lewis, R. S.: *The Other Child*. New York, Grune and Stratton, 1951.

Luria, A. R.: *The Role of Speech in the Regulation of Normal and Abnormal Behavior*. New York, Liveright Publishing Co., 1961.

Machover, K.: *Personality Projection in the Drawing of the Human Figure*. Springfield, Thomas, 1959.

Miller, M. H., and Polisar, I. A.: *Auditory Evaluation of the Pediatric Patient*. Springfield, Thomas, 1964.

Montessori, M.: *The Montessori Method*. New York, Schocken Books, 1964.

Myklebust, H. R.: *Auditory Disorders in Children*. New York, Grune and Stratton, 1954.

Piaget, J.: *The Psychology of Intelligence*. London, Routledge and Kegan, 1947.

Vigotsky, L. S.: *Thought and Language*. The MIT Press, 1962.

Werner, H., and Kaplan, B.: *Symbol Formation*. New York, Wiley & Sons, 1963.

Appendix 3

EDUCATIONAL MATERIALS

Following are some of the materials used in Joan's training program. They are listed from the simplest to the most difficult in those categories where there is progression.

TOYS

Child Guidance Toys, Inc., New York, N. Y.
Fisher Price Toys, Inc., East Aurora, N.Y.
Holgate Toys, Inc., 3720 N. Kedzie Ave., Chicago 18, Ill.
Playskool Mfg. Co., 3720 N. Kedzie Ave., Chicago 18, Ill.
Jig Saw Puzzles
 Playskool, Sifo, Doepke

RECORDS

Tom Glaser Pram Records—First Music for Ones and Twos
Where Are Your Eyes
Bye Bye
Big and Little
Sleepy Time
Toys
Nice

DICTIONARIES

The Golden Dictionary—A Giant Golden Book: Ellen Wales Walpole, Simon and Schuster, Rockefeller Center, New York 20, N. Y.

True to Life ABC Book: Grosset and Dunlap, New York.

Young Reader's Color Picture Dictionary: Margaret B. Parke, Ed.D., Grosset and Dunlap, New York.

Animals—A Blue Angel Picture Dictionary: I. A. Lewis, Samuel Gabriel Sons and Co., New York.

The Golden Picture Book of Words: Jane Werner, Simon and Schuster, N. Y.

SENSE TRAINING MATERIAL

The Montessori Material, Creative Playthings, New York.

WORD GAMES

Lottos
Farm: No. 104, Ed-U-Cards Mfg. Corp., L.I.C., N. Y.
ABC: Ed-U-Cards Mfg. Corp.
Look and Learn: No. 4702-1, Milton Bradley Co., Springfield, Mass.
Go Together: No. 121, Ed-U-Cards Mfg. Corp.
The World Around Us: No. 115, Ed-U-Cards Mfg. Corp.
What's Missing: No. 120, Ed-U-Cards Mfg. Corp.
Picture Words For Beginners: No. 9508, Milton Bradley Co., Springfield, Mass.
Play Way Alphabet Flash Cards, The Gelles-Widmer Co., St. Louis 5, Mo.
Go-Fish—A consonant sound game, Remedial Education Center, Washington, D. C.
Sentence Builder: No. 9512, Milton Bradley Co.
Look—A Play Way Word Bingo Game: No. 1203: Edward P. Dolch, The Gelles-Widmer Co.
Crossword Puzzles: Compiled by Charles Preston, Treasure Books, 1107 Broadway, N. Y.
Grades 2-5 Crossword Puzzles
Animal Crossword Puzzles
Famous People Crossword Puzzles
Crosswords For Kids: Compiled by Jeff E. Thompson, Doubleday and Co., Inc., Garden City, N. Y.
Scrabble For Juniors, Selchow and Righter Company, N. Y.
Educational Password, Milton Bradley Company.
Educational Concentration, Milton Bradley Company.

NUMBER CONCEPT MATERIAL

Structural Arithmetic: Catherine Stern, Houghton Mifflin Co., Boston, Mass.

NUMBER GAMES

Understanding Numbers: No. 9517, Combination and Perception Cards, Milton Bradley Company.

Flash Cards, Addition and Subtraction: No. 9372, Milton Bradley Co.

Fractions: No. 9504, Milton Bradley Co.

ACTIVITY BOOKS

Help Yourself Series, Whitman Publishing Co., Racine, Wis.
Count, Color, Play: Jan Alexander Kiley.
Stories to Read—Pictures to Color—Games to Play: Gladys M. Horn.
Beginning Arithmetic: Gladys M. Horn.
Fun with Writing: Gladys M. Horn.
See it, Say it, Do it: Gladys M. Horn.
Fun with Phonics: Gladys M. Horn.
Quizzle Book of Things that Move: Irma and George Wilde, Samuel Gabriel Sons and Co., New York, N. Y.

I Learn My Numbers, A Blue Angel Picture Book, Samuel Gabriel Sons and Company, New York, N. Y.

Tell Time Clock Book, A Book that Jack Built.

Hart Publishing Company, Inc., Garden City, N. Y.

Playbook for Small Fry: Marion Jollison.

Playtime and Storytime: Carol M. Lane.

It's Fun to Learn: Marion Jollison.

Teach Me Numbers: Mary K. Winters.

100 Learning Games: Rose Marie Stromberg.

Hooray for Play: Jack B. Crawford.

Fun and Puzzles: Lazlo Roth, Harvey House, Inc., Irvington-on-Hudson, New York, N. Y.

Big Book of Pencil Games: Homer M. Peterson, Doubleday and Co., Inc., New York, N. Y.

STORY BOOKS

My Own Little House: Merriman B. Kaune, Follett Publishing Co., Chicago, Ill.

Little Golden Books, Simon and Schuster, Rockefeller Center, New York 20, N. Y.

The Animals of Farmer Jones: Leah Gale.

Baby Animals: Garth Williams.

Guess who Lives Here: Louise Woodcock.

What am I: Ruth Leon.

How Big: Corinne Malvern.

Come Play House: Edith Osswald.

Baby's House: Gelola McHugh.

I Can Fly: Ruth Krause.

Daddies: Janet Frank.

When You Were a Baby: Rita Eng.

Frosty the Snowman: Annie North Bedford.

Fix it Please: Lucy Sprague Mitchell.

A Day at the Zoo: Marion Conger.

The Pokey Little Puppy: Janette Sebring Lowrey.

The Blowaway Hat: Leone Adelson.

Noises and Mr. Flibberty-Jib: Gertrude Crampton.

Mr. Dog: Margaret Wise Brown.

Nursery Rhymes: Gertrude Elliot.

Five Pennies to Spend: Miriam Young.

Let's Save Money: Loyta Higgins.

Let's Go Shopping: Lenore Combes.

A Year in the City: Lucy Sprague Mitchell.

The Very Little Girl: Phyllis Krasilovsky, Doubleday and Company, Inc., Garden City, New York.

Wonder Books, Inc. 1107 Broadway, New York, N. Y.

The Happy Birthday Present: Barbara Bates.

Peter Goes to School: Wanda Rogers House.

The Baby Elephant: Benjamin Brewster.

The Puppy who Found a Boy: George and Irma Wilde.

Ding Dong School Books, Rand McNally and Co., Chicago
  I Decided: Dr. Frances R. Horwich and Reinald Werrenrath, Jr.
  Debbie and Her Nap: Horwich and Werrenrath, Jr.
  My Big Brother: Horwich and Werrenrath, Jr.
Mother Goose, A Big Golden Book: Corinne Malvern, Simon Schuster, New York.
  I Know a Story: Miriam Blanton Huber, Frank Seely Salisbury, and Mabel O'Donnell, Row, Peterson and Co., Evanston, Ill.
  Read-to-Me Story Book: Compiled by the Child Study Association of America, Thomas Y. Crowell Co., N. Y.
  The Adventures of Ulysses: Gerald Gottlieb, Random House, N. Y.
  Book of Greek Myths: Ingri and Edgar Parin D'Aulaire, Doubleday and Company, Inc., Garden City, N. Y.

SOME OF JOAN'S FAVORITE BOOKS

Story Books:
  The Taxi that Hurried: Lucy Sprague Mitchell, Irma Simonton Black, and Jessie Stanton, A Little Golden Book.

  Little Boy with a Big Horn: Jack Bechdolt, A Little Golden Book.

  Peek in: Horwich and Werrenrath, Ding Dong School.

  Julius: Syd Hoff, Harper and Brothers, New York.

  A Fly Went by: Mike McClintock, Random House, N. Y.

  The Cat in the Hat: Dr. Seuss, Random House, N. Y.

  Madeline: Ludwig Bemelmans, Simon and Schuster, N. Y.

  Rusty Rings a Bell: Franklyn M. Branley and Eleanor K. Vaughan, Thomas Y. Crowell Co., N. Y.

  Curious George Gets a Medal: H. A. Rey, Houghton Mifflin Company, Boston.

Walt Disney Books, Simon and Schuster, New York.
  Perri
  Peter Pan
Dr. Seuss Books, Random House, New York.
  Sleep Book, Yertle the Turtle and other stories, How the Grinch Stole Christmas, The Sneetches, and other stories.
  The 500 Hats of Bartholomew Cubbins: Dr. Seuss, The Vanguard Press, New York, N. Y.
  Blaze Finds the Trail: C. W. Anderson, The MacMillan Company, New York, N. Y.
  The Adventures of Peter Cottontail: Thornton W. Burgess, Grosset and Dunlap, New York, N. Y.
  Bobbsey Twin Series: Laura Lee Hope, Grosset and Dunlap, New York, N. Y.
  The Wizard of Oz: L. Frank Baum, Grosset and Dunlap.

Charlotte's Web: E. B. White, Harper and Bros., New York, N.Y.

Little House in the Big Woods: Laura Ingalls Wilder, Harper and Row, New York, N.Y.

The Story of Dr. Dolittle: Hugh Lofting, J. B. Lippincott Co., Philadelphia and New York.

Mary Poppins: P. L. Travers, Harcourt, Brace, and World, Inc., New York, N.Y.

Science Books

The How and Why Wonder Books, Grosset and Dunlap, N. Y.

Rocks and Minerals: Nelson W. Hyler.

Sea Shells: Donald F. Low.

Birds: Robert Mathewson.

The Human Body: Martin Keen.

Allabout Books, Random House, New York, N. Y.

Volcanoes and Earthquakes: Frederick H. Pough.

The Ice Age: Patricia Lauber.

Strange Beasts of the Past: Roy Chapman Andrews.

Golden Books, Golden Press, N. Y.

The Giant Golden Book of Birds: Robert Porter Allen.

The Giant Golden Book of Dinosaurs: Jane Werner Watson.

The Golden Book of Science: Bertha Morris Parker.

The Golden Book of Facts and Figures: Bertha Morris Parker.

Questions and Answers: Horace Elmo.

The Golden Geography: Elsa Jane Werner, Simon and Schuster, N. Y.

The Wonderful World of Archaeology: Ronald Jessup, Garden City Books, Garden City, N. Y.

SCHOOL TEXTS

Reading Readiness:

Readiness for Reading: Edward W. Dolch, Marguerite P. Dolch, and Beulah F. Jackson, The Garrard Press, Champaign, Ill.

Here We Go: Emmett A. Betts, Row, Peterson and Co., Evanston, Ill.

Come and See: Leila Armstrong and Josephine van Dolzen Pease, Follett Publishing Co., N. Y.

Pre-Primers

Scott Foresman and Company, Chicago, Ill.

Ginn and Company, Boston, Mass.

World Book Company, Yonkers-on-Hudson, N. Y.

D. C. Heath and Company, Boston, Mass.

Phonics We Use: Meighen, Pratt, Halvorsen, —Lyons and Carnahan, Chicago, Ill.

Elementary Reading

The New Basic Readers, Grades 1-6, Scott Foresman and Co., Chicago, Ill.

Ginn Basic Readers, Grades 1-6, Ginn and Company, Boston, Mass.

Science

Singer Science Series: George Willard Frasier, Helen Dolman Mac-Cracken, Donald Gilmore Decker, The L. W. Singer Co., Inc., Syracuse, N. Y.

Seeing New Things, Grade 2.
Finding Answers, Grade 3
Science in Your Life, Grade 4.
Science in Our World, Grade 5.
Science for Today and Tomorrow, Grade 6, Herman and Nina Schneider,
    D. C. Heath and Co., Boston, Mass.
Number Readiness.
    Jolly Numbers Primer: Buswell, Brownell, and John, Ginn and Co.,
        Boston, Mass.
    Happy Times with Numbers: Evelyn Fershing, Allen and Bacon, Inc.,
        N. Y.
Arithmetic
    Scott Foresman and Company, Chicago, Ill.
    World Book Company, Yonkers-on-Hudson, N. Y.
    Row, Peterson and Company, Evanston, Ill.

ADDITIONAL EDUCATIONAL MATERIALS

Practice Workbook of Reading, Grades 1-4.
Practice Workbook of Spelling, Grades 1-4.
Practice Workbook of English, Grades 2-3: Treasure Books, Inc., 1107
    Broadway, N. Y.
Reading Skill Builder: Reader's Digest Services, Inc., Educational
    Division, Pleasantville, N. Y.
Practice Exercises in Reading, Books III-VI: Arthur I. Gates and
    Celeste Comegys Peardon, Bureau of Publications, Teachers College,
    Columbia University, N. Y.
Standard Test Lessons in Reading, Books A-E: McCall-Crabbs, Bureau
    of Publications, Teachers College, Columbia University, N. Y.
*How to Help Your Child in Reading, Writing, and Arithmetic, Grades
    1-6:* Frieda E. Van Atta, Random House, N. Y.